PUZZLES
BRAINTEASERS

GYLES BRANDRETH'S BOOK OF

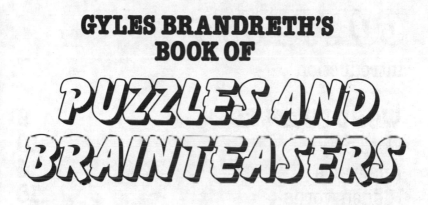

PUZZLES AND BRAINTEASERS

CONTENTS

First published in 1982 by
Octopus Books Limited
59 Grosvenor Street
London W1

Second impression, 1983

ISBN 0 86273 047 3

Printed and bound in Great Britain by
Collins Glasgow

Illustrations by Ellis Nadler
Russell Barnett
Andrew Martin
Paul Davies
Brian Mayor

INTRODUCTION

At school I had a teacher whose name – I promise you – was
Justin Thyme. Though he taught geography for a living, he
really lived not for his work but for his hobby which was
collecting, devising and solving puzzles. I had him very much in
mind while compiling this book because it contains all the kinds
of puzzles he enjoyed most: word puzzles, number puzzles,
picture puzzles, puzzles involving coins and dominoes and
matchsticks. Mr Thyme liked plenty of variety in his puzzles and
I know it would have delighted him to come across a book that
included puzzles as amazing as most of our mazes (page 84), as
baffling as some of our Brainteasers (page 90) and as unusual as
all our Tangrams (page 140).

Every puzzle in the book has been given a star rating. The
one-star puzzles are the easiest. The two-star puzzles are rather
more taxing. And even Mr Thyme might find the three-star
puzzles something of a challenge. I hope you enjoy them all.
And to put you in the right mood let me start you off with one of
Mr Thyme's favourites. He would come into the classroom, call
for silence and then announce his Proverb of the Day:

**A slight inclination of the cranium is as adequate
as a spasmodic movement of one optic to an equine
quadruped utterly devoid of any visionary capacity.**

What on earth was he trying to say?

Gyles Brandreth.

P.S. You will find the answer to Mr Thyme's puzzle with all the
others at the back of the book.

WORD PUZZLES

Simple Start*

The longest word in the Oxford English Dictionary is this one:

PNEUMONOULTRAMICROSCOPICSILICOVOLCANOCONIOSIS

It is a 45 letter word that is the alleged name of a disease supposedly contracted from breathing in fine volcanic dust.

Here are some more words that are neither so long nor so difficult, but can you work out what each one means?

Verbal Display*

1. What is **to hustle?**
   Is it: a) to push and hurry? ✓
   b) to go to sleep?
   c) to jump high in the air?
   d) to round up cattle?

2. What is **to brawl?**
   Is it: a) to sail a yacht? ✗
   b) to sing loudly?
   c) to fight? ✓
   d) to cook?

3. What is **to gratify?**
   Is it: a) to grate cheese?
   b) to laugh?
   c) to catch a cold?
   d) to please?

4. What is **to munch?**
   Is it: a) to be sick?
   b) to eat? ✓
   c) to spit?
   d) to drink?

5. What is **to repulse?**
   Is it: a) to drive off an attack? ✓
   b) to take a pulse for a second time?

c) to steal money?
d) to faint at the sight of blood?

6. What is **to submerge?**
   Is it: a) to climb mountains?
   b) to lift great weights?
   c) to go under water? ✓
   d) to open a bank account?

7. What is **to distort?**
   Is it: a) to make something straight?
   b) to make something die?
   c) to put something out of shape? ✓
   d) to bounce something up and down?

8. What is **to meditate?**
   Is it: a) To visit the Mediterranean?
   b) to administer medicine?
   c) to paint a picture?
   d) to think deeply? ✓

9. What is **to wallop?**
   Is it: a) to serve ice-cream?
   b) to hit someone or something? ✓
   c) to bite someone or something?
   d) to travel by kangaroo?

10. What is **to somnambulate?**
    Is it: a) to call an ambulance?
    b) to try to fly?
    c) to bury someone alive?
    d) to walk in one's sleep? ✓

10/10

Collecting Collectives***

You probably know that a group of ants is called a colony and a collection of ponies is called a string, but did you know that a mass of larks is known as an **exaltation**? There are collective nouns to describe all sorts of groups of animals. On the next page is a list of some of the most interesting and unusual of these. The collective noun is provided, all you have to do is supply the names of the animals.

To help you the first letter of each of the animal names is given:

1. A shrewdness of a _ _ _
2. A cete of b _ _ _ _ _ _
3. A shoal of b _ _ _
4. A sloth of b _ _ _ _
5. An army of c AJ E RP ILL IL
6. A clowder of c _ _ _
7. A drove of c _ _ _ _ _ _
8. A peep of c _ _ _ _ _ _ _
9. A murder of c _ _ _ _
10. A dule of d _ _ _ _
11. A school of f I S H
12. A skulk of f _ _ _ _
13. A gaggle of g E ES A
14. A husk of h _ _ _ _
15. A cast of h _ _ _ _
16. A brood of h _ _ _
17. A siege of h _ _ _ _ _
18. A haras of h _ _ _ _ _
19. A smack of j _ _ _ _ _ _ _ _
20. A kindle of k _ _ _ _ _ _
21. A deceit of l _ _ _ _ _ _ _
22. A leap of l _ _ _ _ _ _ _
23. A pride of l I O N S
24. A plague of l _ _ _ _ _ _
25. A watch of n _ _ _ _ _ _ _ _ _ _
26. A parliament of o _ _ _

Homophones*

No, homophones aren't telephones you have around the house: they are words that sound alike, but have different spellings or different meanings – like **wholly** (meaning 'completely') and **holy** (meaning 'sacred'). Can you find the homophones that will fit these clues?

1. a. **The opposite of left**   b. **A special kind of ceremony**
   Both words begin with letter R.

2. a. **A group of musicians**   b. **Forbidden**
   Both words begin with B.

3. a. **Corn on the cob**   b. **A Labyrinth you might get lost in.**
   Both words begin with M.

4. a. **To agree**   b. **A climb**
   Both words begin with A.

5. a. **When you break the rules in a sport**
   b. **This is what a chicken is**
   Both words begin with F.

6. a. An agreement   b. What a suitcase is when it's full
   Both words begin with P.   *ACT*
                               PACKED

7. a. A cricketer does it.
   b. You eat soup out of it.   *BOWL*
   Both words begin with B.

8. a. You can bounce it   b. Shout   *BALL*
   Both words begin with B.   *BAWL*

9. a. A river in France   b. Rational health   *SEINE*
   Both words begin with S.   *SANE*

10. a. To put in position   b. A flattened fish.
    Both words begin with P.   *PLACE*
                                PLAICE

WHAT LETTER WOULD BE USEFUL
TO A DEAF WOMAN ?

THE LETTER A BECAUSE IT MAKES
HER HEAR

If you were given the following phrases:
A smart giant, Ma!
Matt sang 'Maria'.
Mama's a ratting.
Gain a smart mat.
apart from the fact that they make little sense, you would probably feel that they have little in common. Wrong! If the letters in each phrase are transposed the word ANAGRAMMATIST can be formulated, which is exactly what you would be if you did so! See how great your skill as an anagrammatist is with the following variety of puzzles.

Head Over Heels*
Take the words **ROAST MULES** and rearrange the ten letters in the words to form a single ten-letter word.

European Cities**
Here are anagrams of 14 European cities. How quickly can you discover their names? (As a clue the country in which you will find the city is given in brackets.)

1. EVINCE (Italy) VENICE
2. PANELS (Italy)
3. HASTEN (Greece) ATHENS
4. MISER (France)
5. ANISE (Italy)
6. SABLE (Switzerland) BASLE
7. PAIRS (France) PARIS
8. ROCK (Eire) CORK
9. SOLO (Norway) OSLO
10. MORE (Italy) ROME
11. ENGLARDIN (USSR)
12. LOOTED (Spain)
13. STONED (Belgium)
14. AVENGE (Switzerland)

World Cities***
Today Europe, tomorrow the world! Unscramble the names of the following cities around the globe. (Again the countries in which you will find the cities are given in brackets.)

1. MINKS (USSR)
2. SAULT (USA)
3. UNITS (Tunisia)
4. GOALS (Nigeria)
5. BAULK (Afghanistan)
6. LOUSE (Vietnam)
7. MAILS (India)
8. MAIL (Peru)
9. NERO (USA)
10. SALVAGES (USA)
11. DIAGNOSE (USA)
12. DOTTIER (USA)
13. JUANITA (Mexico)
14. GRANITE (Morocco)
15. COUNTS (USA)
16. ANTHER (Iran)
17. DRAMAS (India)
18. INWARD (Australia)
19. ANIMAL (Philippines)
20. NERVED (USA)
21. ENCLAVE (France)
22. ANVIL (Lithuania)
23. TOKYO (Japan)
24. RACE (Israel)

Occupy Yourself**

Listed here are 25 different occupations and professions. Occupy yourself in a professional way by trying to unravel them.

1. GALORE
2. LEWDER
3. REWARD
4. THREAT
5. MARINA
6. RIOTED
7. STRIPE
8. RESIGN
9. RIALTO
10. CRANED
11. RETARD
12. STRAIT
13. CORKED
14. APRONS
15. WANDER
16. TROUT
17. MOANS
18. RUNES
19. DRIVE
20. BREAK
21. DREY
22. CASTERS
23. HECTARE
24. LAMINAR
25. STINTED

Gladstone***

The name of the British Prime Minister **WILLIAM EWART GLAD-STONE** can be anagrammed into these relevant phrases:

1. Great wise old man, at will.
2. Go, administrate law well.
3. Wilt tear down all images.
4. Wild agitator means well.

Can you make at least four more phrases?

You Name It**

Here, in anagrammatic form, are the first names of boys and girls.
Can you sort them out?

1. GEM	2. ROAD	3. LINE
4. SMILE	5. OSIER	6. HOARD
7. AURAL	8. GREAT	9. LETHE
10. GRADE	11. AMBLE	12. MAORI
13. IDEAL	14. LILAC	15. ASSET
16. SALLET	17. YONDER	18. DANGLE
19. SINGLY	20. ANTRIM	21. EVENTS
22. RIDING	23. HAMLET	24. EASTER

Problematic Phrases***

Each of the 18 phrases listed here can be turned into one single
word. For example, the phrase **'Often sheds tears'** could become
'softheartedness'. See if you can find the 18 words that make up
these phrases – and the phrases should give you either a cryptic or
a perverse clue to the words you are looking for.

For example, **IS NOT SOLACED** could lead you cryptically to
DISCONSOLATE and **LET MAN LOVE** could lead you perversely to
MALEVOLENT.

1. I HIRE PARSONS	2. REAL FUN
3. FINE TONIC	4. IT'S MORE FUN
5. SEEN AS MIST	6. TENDER NAMES
7. LET'S RUSH	8. A STEW, SIR?
9. OUR MEN EARN IT	10. NINE THUMPS
11. NICE LOVE	12. ILL FED
13. IS IT LEGAL? NO	14. I LIMIT ARMS
15. LIFE'S AIM	16. RESTORE PLUSH
17. A ROPE ENDS IT	18. GOT AS A CLUE

Presidential Poser**

AN ORAL DANGER is a phrase that can be rearranged to give the
name of an American President. Which one?

One Over the Eight**

The sentence below was formed by rearranging the letters of a well known proverb. Which proverb?

THIS IS MEANT AS INCENTIVE

Prime Poser*

THAT GREAT CHARMER is a phrase that can be rearranged to give the name of another unique British Prime Minister. Which one?

In the following puzzles you will find the given words hidden in the square. The words you have got to find may be written forwards or backwards, upwards or downwards or even diagonally.

Alpha Plus*

A is the only vowel you will find on this page. Can you find all 67 of the A words in the square opposite?

AARDVARK	ABRACADABRA	ADAMANT
ADAPT	ALABAMA	ALFALFA
ALMANAC	ALPACA	ALTAR
AMALGAM	ANAGRAM	ARMADA
ARRAS	ASP	ASTRAKHAN
AVATAR	BACCARAT	BALACLAVA
BALD	BANAL	BANANA
BASALT	BAZAAR	BWANA
CABAL	CALABASH	CANADA
CANAL	CANASTA	CANCAN
CANTATA	CARAVAN	CASCARA
CASSAVA	CATAMARAN	CATARACT
CHARABANC	DATA	DRAMA
GALA	GRANADA	HALMA
KRAAL	LAVA	LLAMA
MADAGASCAR	MADAM	MAGNA CARTA
MAHARAJA	MAHATMA	MARACAS
MARSALA	MASCARA	PANAMA
PANDA	PARAGRAPH	PARALLAX
PHALANX	RAMADAN	RATAPLAN
SALAAM	SALAD	SARABAND
SAVANNA	TARMACADAM	VALHALLA
VANDAL		

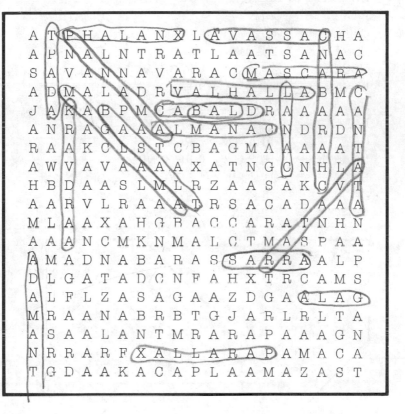

```
A T P H A L A N X L A V A S S A C H A
A P N A L N T R A T L A A T S A N A C
S A V A N N A V A R A C M A S C A R A
A D M A L A D R V A L H A L L A B M C
J A K A B P M C A B A L D R A A A A A
A N R A G A A A L M A N A C N D R D N
R A A K C L S T C B A G M A A A A T
A W V A V A A A A X A T N G C N H L A
H B D A A S L M L R Z A A S A K C V T
A A R V L R A A A T R S A C A D A A A
M L A A X A H G R A C C A R A T N H N
A A A N C M K N M A L C T M A S P A A
A M A D N A B A R A S S A R R A A L P
D L G A T A D C N F A H X T R C A M S
A L F L Z A S A G A A Z D G A A L A G
M R A A N A B R B T G J A R L R L T A
A S A A L A N T M R A R A P A A A G N
N R R A R F X A L L A R A P A M A C A
T G D A A K A C A P L A A M A Z A S T
```

X-Tract**

Extract the following words hidden in the diagram below.

ANNEX	APEX	APPENDIX	BORAX
BOX	CALX	CALYX	CICATRIX
CLIMAX	COAX	COCCYX	CODEX
COMPLEX	CORTEX	COX	CRUX
EQUINOX	FLAX	FLEX	FLUX
FOX	HELIX	HOAX	IBEX
ILEX	INDEX	KEX	LARYNX
LATEX	LYNX	MUREX	ONYX
ORYX	PARADOX	PAX	PHALANX
PHARYNX	PHLOX	PHOENIX	PREFIX
PYX	QUINCUNX	SEX	SPHINX
STYX	SUFFIX	SYNTAX	THORAX
VERTEX	VORTEX	WAX	

```
C X X Y H               X B I C X
O E X E L I             X O N A E X
D B L S T Y X         X R D L K I X
E I Q X X R X E     F A E X A F C Y
X E Q U I N O X T X X I N E O H P
  Y U L X V Y C E R R N R A X C
    X F C N O R X T E P X P X
      Y O W U R A X A V E W
        M M X C T H S L P
      T P X I D N E P P A X
    X H L C O P Y I X A H X H
  F L O E X L C S Y U N R I E X
X O A R X Y L A C U U Q A A N L P
X C R A N I X C   X F X U L D X F
O R Y X M A O       W F Q X A O H
B U N A L C         X I W M H X
X X X F X           X X E S P
```

Quoting the Bard***

You are asked to find in the diagram on page 23 the words which will complete the following quotations from Shakespeare, all of which have become part of everyday speech. Each missing word is denoted by a number of dashes representing the number of letters in the word.

If you are stumped by any of the quotations, a word list is on page 23.

1. '_ _ _ _ _ _ _ is such sweet sorrow' (ROMEO AND JULIET)

2. 'Sweet lovers love the _ _ _ _ _ _' (AS YOU LIKE IT)

3. 'I must be _ _ _ _ _, only to be kind' (HAMLET)

4. 'More sinned against than _ _ _ _ _ _ _ _ _' (KING LEAR)

5. 'A _ _ _ _ _ _ _ on both your houses' (ROMEO AND JULIET)

6. 'Though this be madness, yet there is _ _ _ _ _ _ in it' (HAMLET)

7. 'For this _ _ _ _ _ _ much thanks' (HAMLET)

8 'The time is out of _ _ _ _ _' (HAMLET)

9. 'There's a _ _ _ _ _ _ _ _ that shapes our ends' (HAMLET)

10. 'it did me yeoman's _ _ _ _ _ _ _' (HENRY IV PART i)

11. ''Twas _ _ _ _ _ _ _ to the general' (HAMLET)

12. 'When we have shuffled off this mortal _ _ _ _' (HAMLET)

13. 'For mine own part, it was _ _ _ _ _ to me' (JULIUS CAESAR)

14. 'The wheel is come full _ _ _ _ _ _' (KING LEAR)

15. '_ _ _ _ _ _ _ in stones' (AS YOU LIKE IT)

16. 'Sweet are the uses of _ _ _ _ _ _ _ _ _' (AS YOU LIKE IT)

17. 'I have not slept one _ _ _ _' (CYMBELINE)

18. '_ _ _ _ _ _ _ _ _ _ doth make cowards of us all' (HAMLET)

19. 'They come not single spies, but in _ _ _ _ _ _ _ _ _ _'
(HAMLET)

20. 'And thereby hangs a _ _ _ _' (AS YOU LIKE IT)

21. 'Well said; that was laid on with a _ _ _ _ _ _'
(AS YOU LIKE IT)

22. 'I could a tale _ _ _ _ _ _' (HAMLET)

23. 'A good deed in a _ _ _ _ _ _ _ world'
(THE MERCHANT OF VENICE)

24. 'The world's mine _ _ _ _ _ _'
(THE MERRY WIVES OF WINDSOR)

25. 'But I will wear my heart upon my _ _ _ _ _ _' (OTHELLO)

26. 'An _ _ _ _ _ _ _ _ _ _ _ thing, sir, but mine own'
(AS YOU LIKE IT)

27. 'Neither a _ _ _ _ _ _ _ _ nor a _ _ _ _ _ _ be' (HAMLET)

28. '_ _ _ _ _ _ _ is the soul of _ _ _' (HAMLET)

29. 'He hath eaten me out of _ _ _ _ _ and _ _ _ _'
(HENRY IV PART ii)

30. 'Thy _ _ _ _ was father, Harry, to the _ _ _ _ _ _ _'
(HENRY IV PART ii)

31. 'More in _ _ _ _ _ _ than in _ _ _ _ _' (HAMLET)

32. '_ _ _ _ _ _ and ministers of _ _ _ _ _ defend us' (HAMLET)

33. 'The _ _ _ _ _ _ of true _ _ _ _ never did run _ _ _ _ _ _'
(A MID-SUMMER NIGHT'S DREAM)

Parting	Spring	Cruel	Sinning
Plague	Method	Relief	Joint
Divinity	Service	Caviare	Coil
Greek	Circle	Sermons	Adversity
Wink	Conscience	Battalions	Tale
Trowel	Unfold	Naughty	Oyster
Sleeve	Ill-favoured	Borrower	Lender
Brevity	Wit	House	Home
Wish	Thought	Sorrow	Anger
Angels	Grace	Course	Love
Smooth			

```
T H I L V B E V O L B R U D T S G L E
F E I L E R M O V A G Y N A S R K Y S
U P V I L C O Y T I W H F N C H M B U
H T N E B F H T R V O D O H T E M T O
S T A B E R A I V A C M L O D H B E H
Y E O N O L J V I C R G D N W A R C T
T H E O I W S E O E V H A L O J I A B
J U C O M I T R S U G V I G R O G R Y
S K N I W S Y B O R R O W E R V E G B
D S E D T H D R G E E E K E O T J I O
I P I T T Y T I S R E V D A S D M N A
S R C C S M L O V Y K N A Y G L E I G
C I S P E Y H L L I E M O A N G E L S
R N N T R C T C E L N R E G N A S T O
E G O N V W I H C W D I V I Z C R A M
N T C H I R T H G U O H T O C R U E L
A L A Y C N O C L U Y R P Y F L O J I
J O O L E U G A L P A B T A A N C B O
H R E J E L I F I P T N I O J I N A C
```

Parlez-vous?**

You don't have to be French to find the following words in the
diagram opposite:

A LA CARTE

APERITIF

AU REVOIR

BETE NOIRE

BISTRO

BON VIVEUR

BOUILLON

BOUTIQUE

CHEF

COIFFEUR

CORDON BLEU

CROUTON

ENCORE

ENNUI

ESPRIT DE CORPS

FAUX PAS

GAUCHE

HORS DE COMBAT

MASSEUR

NEGLIGEE

NOM DE PLUME

ROTISSERIE

VINGT-ET-UN

AMOUR

ART NOUVEAU

AVOIRDUPOIS

BIJOU

BONHOMIE

BON VOYAGE

BOURGEOIS

CHAUFFEUR

CHERCHEZ LA FEMME

COR ANGLAIS

COUTURE

CUISINE

ENFANT TERRIBLE

ENTREE

FAIT ACCOMPLI

GATEAU

GRAND PRIX

MAL DE MER

MATINEE

NOBLESSE OBLIGE

PIED-A-TERRE

SAVOIR-FAIRE

VIN ORDINAIRE

```
G R N C E V L C H A N G L E U Q I T U O B
R U N O L L I U O B A I R S T P U E L E Y
F E L I B G R N O R E V U A I R L E G I C
R F A U I L R U O M A R O E N B A A S H X
U F I O R E E E U R U N D I N D Y C E A O
E U A J N G E S P E D A C O R O P R A I S
V A H I E R O N S Y T I D L V D C R O L T
I H U B T W R S I E X R N N A H U C I F A
V C A N T A A I R T O S O A E I U P H X S
N F E O N M C R O U A R U Z I I S E O P Q
O L V O A V E C H V U M L Y S R O R R I U
B B U U F L U I O S E A T I E U E O S I S
E O O T N M G I R M F R N M G H C C D U A
T N N U E B R F F E P E U G H E T N E N F
E I T R R F L I M O S L E A D J O E C N X
N O R E A G T M O P P S I T E N G L O E U
O M A I D I E R U E F F I O C I A T M B A
I I R U R G L O D P I R C T L E U A B I F
R E M E D L A M I B P S H G O O C H A N C
E M P R A V O R T S I B E I R R H O T L E
D A R V I N G T E T U N F C U A E T A G O
```

The Haystack***

Can you find the word **NEEDLE**? It appears only once.

```
E L D E N E E D E L N E E N E D L
L E E N E D L E N E E D E L N E E
D E E L E N D L E E D E N E E D L
E D N E L E E N E L   E E L E E N E
N E E L D E E D N L E D E N D E N
E N L E E D E L E D E E N E L E L
E E D E N N E E L E D L E N D E E
D E D E L E E D N E E L D E L L D
N L E N E L D L E N E E L D N E E
E D E D L N E E E D L E N E E D L
L E L D E L N E L E N E D E D N E
N E E D N E D E D E E D E N L E L
N E L D E E E E L N E E L E D E E
N E D E L D E N E E D L N E E L D
E N D E E L E N E N E E L D E E E
E L E N N E E E D L E N E E L N N
E E D L E N E L E N E L E N E N D
```

CIPHERS AND FRIENDS

What is the difference between a code and a cipher? Many people talk of 'secret codes' when they really mean 'secret ciphers'. Strictly speaking, a cipher is a system whereby every letter in the alphabet is replaced by another letter, number or symbol. A code is a system whereby one single word, letter or symbol can represent a whole sentence. Most of the following puzzles are designed to test your deciphering skills.

Two of a Kind**

Here are the names of two people we associate with a particular time of the year. Can you decipher their names?

1. KFTVT DISJTU   2. TBOUB DMBVT

Film Fun**

The sequences of vowels and dashes below are the titles of various popular films. The consonants have been missed out, hence:
_ _E _A_ _E _E_E would be **THE WAY WE WERE**
Fill in the missing consonants.

1. _ _E _OU_ O_ _U_L
2. O_E _ _E_ O_E_ _ _E _U_ _OO_ _E_ _
3. _ _E _ _E_ _ _ IEU_E_A_ _ _ _O_A_
4. _ _A_ _A_ _
5. _A_U_ _A_ _L_ _ _ _E_E_
6. E_L U_ _E_ _ _E _U_
7. _ _A_IO_ _ O_ _LE
8. _U_E_ _A
9. A_LA_ _OU_E
10. _O_ _OU_ E_E_ O_ _ _

Word Numbers*

One cipher used by secret agents replaces letters with numbers. In a simple version of this **A** becomes **1**, **B** becomes **2**, and so on, with **Z** being **26**. The following words are in a number cipher, but **A** is **3**, **B** is **4**, and so on. Can you decipher the words?

1. 20 7 5 22 11 8 27
2. 18 3 22 20 11 3 20 5 10
3. 10 7 20 3 14 6
4. 9 20 17 22 7 21 19 23 7
5. 24 7 16 22 11 14 3 22 7
6. 22 20 7 15 23 14 17 23 21
7. 21 16 11 9 9 7 20
8. 20 7 23 16 11 17 16
9. 18 20 17 22 7 11 16
10. 15 17 16 21 22 20 17 23 21
11. 14 23 15 11 16 3 20 27
12. 11 6 11 17 21 27 16 5 20 3 21 27
13. 8 20 23 21 22 20 3 22 7
14. 6 20 3 23 9 10 22 21 15 3 16
15. 6 11 21 22 3 16 5 7

Novel Quiz**

These ten book titles are written without any vowels. Can you insert vowels amongst the consonants to form the titles **and** name the author of the work in each instance?

1.	BLK HS	2.	NNTN GHTY FR
3.	MM	4.	JN YR
5.	WNN TH PH	6.	PRSSN
7.	TH TL F PTR RBBT	8.	FRM RSS WTH LV
9.	FRNKNSTN	10.	LTTL WMN

Sounds Familiar*

These letters represent a conversation that took place recently in an East European hotel between two secret agents. One was posing as a waiter, the other was ordering breakfast. Both spoke in English, but with unusual accents. What did they say?

F U N E X ?

S V F X

F U N E M ?

S V F M

O K L F M N X

Mixed Faith***

The following jumbled quotations are all taken from the Bible. Can you rearrange them to read their original meaning?

1. Thou servant good and well, faithful done.
   (St Matthew Ch. 25 v. 23)

2. Over his love was me banner.
   (Song of Solomon Ch. 2 v. 4)

3. Am am I I that.
   (Exodus Ch. 3 v. 14)

4. Escaped I am with the teeth skin of my.
   (Job Ch. 19 v. 20)

5. But a sword came I not to send peace.
   (St Matthew Ch. 10 v. 34)

6. Hear hear that let ears to him hath he.
   (St Mark Ch. 4. v. 9)

7. Not him received own his and own his unto came he.
   (St John Ch. 1 v. 11)

8. In hope believed hope against who.
   (Romans Ch. 4 v. 18)

9. I I have have written written what.
   (St John Ch. 19 v. 22)

10. Yea nay yea nay and let your your be.
    (James Ch. 5 v. 12)

11. After his own heart a man.
    (1 Samuel Ch. 13 v. 14)

False Start*
Can you understand this message?

GALLB GTHEY RFIRSTQ

HANDX TALLY STHEJ
KLASTH YLETTERSN

WARET PFALSEM

Vowel Play**
In ye olden days people were encouraged to keep the ten commandments by learning this rhyming couplet. Add the same missing vowel in the appropriate places and see if you can make sense of the couplet today.

PRSVR Y PRFCT MN
VR KP THS PRCPTS TN

Unnatural Break*
What does this message say?

AL LOU RLIV ESWEA RECRU SHE DBYTHEWEI GHTOFW ORDS

Alphabetical Extractions***

The words below have each had a different letter removed wherever it occurs in the word. One word has had two or more A's extracted, one word has had two or more B's extracted, and so on through the alphabet. Thus FLUFFY might appear as LUY. Can you discover the 26 original words.

1. VRGRN	2. RYTM	3. INIU	4. UINUIREME
5. NGRM	6. IETEE	7. ARLIN	8. IGAM
9. YLI	10. UIES	11. INY	12. GPS
13. UCCE	14. ERES	15. HIRY	16. ANARE
17. EASIE	18. SUUR	19. HOO	20. IABE
21. JAY	22. AMNE	23. LLATE	24. EUNE
25. VD	26. RONC		

The Word***

Here is an English word with ecclesiastical associations. It isn't very common, but if you know your Roman numerals you should find it easy. It can be found in any dictionary.

E10100010001000UN1100ATXN

Full Marx*

What do you need to make sense of these letters? Movie buffs will love this puzzle.

1. NML CRCKRS	2. MNKY BSNSS	3. HRS FTHRS
4. DCK SP	5. NGHT T TH PR	6. DY T TH RCS

WHAT OCCURS ONCE IN A MINUTE, TWICE IN A MOMENT, BUT NOT ONCE IN A HUNDRED YEARS?

THE LETTER M.

WORD CIRCLES AND LADDERS AND SQUARES

Word Circles***

Each circle of letters makes up a familiar eight letter word, written in either a clockwise or an anticlockwise direction. Identify all 16 words as quickly as you can.

1.
```
    R
 C     E
I       
 O
  N
```

2.
```
    T I
 A     
I       
 C      
  S
```

3.
```
  M   N
 A     C
  L     Y
   C
```

4.
```
     E
  V     R
 E       B
  I       E
   L
```

5.
```
  E
 M     
O       
 R     
  D
```

6.
```
    S
 R     
O       
 N     T
    A
```

7.
```
  E
 R     O
 U     L
  I     A
   C     N
    G
     I
```

8.
```
     S
  T     Y
 E       H
  R       C
    I
```

9.
```
   M
 R     O
A       N
 H     I
    C
```

10.
```
   L
 E     Y
O       A
 G     G
    R
```

11.
```
    I T
 C     
 S     
  L    Y
   M
```

12.
```
   A    H
 S     A
 I     D
    E  N
```

13.
```
  N
 E     
M       
 O     
    N
```

14.
```
   T
 M     E
C       M
 I     R
    R
    O
```

15.
```
    N
 A     G
P       L
 R     
 H     
  E    Y
    C
```

16.
```
    O
 L     G
     I
U       
 E     S
    T
```

Magic Spell***

One of the best-known 'magic' words must be **ABRACADABRA**. In centuries gone by the word was used as a magic charm to ward off evil spirits. The word would be written on parchment and hung around the neck. A popular way of writing the charm was like this:

```
        A
       B B
      R R R
     A A A A
    C C C C C
   A A A A A A
  D D D D D D D
 A A A A A A A A
B B B B B B B B B
R R R R R R R R R R
A A A A A A A A A A A
```

See if you can count the number of ways it is possible to spell out the word **ABRACADABRA** on such an amulet, by starting from the A at the top and always proceeding from one letter to an adjacent one. You can move diagonally to the left or right and change direction after each letter.

Six-Letter Odd-Ends**

Here are 42 familiar six-letter words with uncommon endings.
Can you supply the missing letters to complete the words?

1. ___ODA	2. ___HMA	3. ___RUB
4. ___HID	5. ___IOD	6. ___URD
7. ___EXE	8. ___ALF	9. ___ULF
10. ___ZOI	11. ___GEL	12. ___FIL
13. ___SUL	14. ___THM	15. ___TIM
16. ___HOM	17. ___XEN	18. ___EMN
19. ___EBO	20. ___CCO	21. ___OCO
22. ___REO	23. ___DIO	24. ___AMO
25. ___KOO	26. ___RYO	27. ___AAR
28. ___UAR	29. ___EOR	30. ___UOR
31. ___HYR	32. ___VAS	33. ___GIS
34. ___GAT	35. ___IAT	36. ___VAT
37. ___DAU	38. ___OLU	39. ___VEX
40. ___AXY	41. ___NTZ	42. ___RTZ

Bird Fivers*

Take a letter from each bird in turn to spell another 5-letter bird.

```
F   I   N   C   H

G   R   E   B   E

E   A   G   L   E

S   N   I   P   E

H   E   R   O   N
```

In for a Spell**

The word square below is made up of 25 letters of the alphabet,
omitting the letter Q. Start at any of the letters and moving one
letter at a time (up, down, right, left, or diagonally) see how many
different words you can spell out. Do not use any letter more than

once in the same word. You can change direction after each letter. All words must be of at least three letters, and no proper names, plurals, abbreviations or foreign words can be used. Aim for a minimum of 20 words.

```
A   B   C   D   E

J   I   H   G   F

K   L   M   N   O

U   T   S   R   P

V   W   X   Y   Z
```

Musical Spell***

In the network below the names of 14 musical instruments are hidden. To spell out the instruments you can start from any letter, and the consecutive letters of the word will be contained in adjacent cells connected horizontally, vertically or diagonally.

```
F   I   N   V   O

L   E   P   I   L

U   T   R   M   A

A   B   U   D   N

M   O   E   G   O
```

Fill-ins**

With this puzzle all you have to do is fill in the blanks__ and to help you, in each puzzle, it's the same letters that are missing from each line. Here's an example:

```
          T__
          _T_
          __T
```

All you've got to do is think of the two letters that are missing from each line and, when you've thought of them, fill them in. Since abbreviations aren't allowed it won't take you long to realise that **E** and **A** are the missing letters in the example and that, filled in, the puzzle looks like this:

>   **TEA**
>   **ATE**
>   **EAT**

Here's another, more difficult one:

>   _ _ P
>   _ P _
>   P _ _

The missing letters are **T** and **A**, so it looks like this:

>   **TAP**
>   **APT**
>   **PAT**

Now you've got the idea, see how you get on with these:

1. R _ _	**2.** S _ _ S·	**3.** C _ _ _ S
_ R_	_ S_ S	S C _ _ _
_ _ R	_ _ S S	_ _ C_ S
	S _ _ S	

4. R I _ _ _ _	**5.** _ _ A M_	**6.** P _ _ T
_ R I _ _ _	_ _ _ A M	P _ T_
_ _ R I _ _	M_ A _ _	T _ P_
	M A _ _ _	_ T_ P
	_ A M _ _	_ P_ T

7. _ O O _	**8.** _ E _ D
_ O_ O	D _ _ E
_ O O_	_ _ D E

Word Ladders***

Lewis Carroll introduced us to Word Ladders. The idea is a simple one. For example, you might be asked to change APE into MAN by altering one letter at a time, without altering the position of the other letters, and always leaving a true word as the link word:

APE
APT
OPT
OAT
MAT
MAN

Here are some of the best of Lewis Carroll's own Word Ladder challenges:

1. Drive **PIG** into **STY** with four links.

2. Raise **FOUR** to **FIVE** with six links.

3. Make **WHEAT** into **BREAD** with six links.

4. Touch **NOSE** with **CHIN** with five links.

5. Change **TEARS** INTO **SMILE** with five links.

6. Make **HARE** into **SOUP** with six links.

7. **PITCH TENTS** with five links.

8. Cover **EYE** with **LID** with three links.

9. Prove **PITY** to be **GOOD** with six links.

10. Turn **POOR** into **RICH** with five links.

11. Get **WOOD** from **TREE** with seven links.

12. Prove **GRASS** to be **GREEN** with seven links.

13. Make **FLOUR** into **BREAD** with five links.

14. Make **TEA HOT** with three links.

15. Get **COAL** from **MINE** with five links.

16. Change **BLACK** to **WHITE** with six links.

17. Turn **WITCH** into **FAIRY** with 12 links.

18. Make **WINTER SUMMER** with 13 links.

INTERNATIONAL WORDWAYS

Ici Français**

There are many French words and phrases that have almost become part of everyday English. Here are a few. Do you know what they mean?

1. A bientôt
2. Adieu
3. Affair de coeur
4. Aide de camp
5. A la mode
6. Au fait
7. Avant garde
8. Bijou
9. Billet doux
10. Blasé
11. Cartouche
12. Chacun à son gôut
13. Coup de grâce
14. Décolletage
15. Déjà vu
16. Mot juste
17. Nom de guerre
18. Outré
19. Passé
20. Risqué

HOW CAN YOU SAY 'I AM LOOKING FOR YOU' IN 3 LETTERS?

Hidden Countries**

The names of two countries are hidden in each of the ten sentences below. Can you discover them? For instance, in the sentence 'Interpol and the FBI discover hidden marksmen', **POLAND** is concealed in the first two words and **DENMARK** is concealed in the last two words.

1. Vladimir and Olga are Soviet names.

2. Have you ever heard an animal talk in dialect?

3. In letters to the press we denounce the wholesale ban on luxury imports.

4. Evening classes may help an amateur to improve his painting.

5. Children put on galoshes to go out in the rain.

6. Rash decisions may cause trouble so thorough analysis is a necessity.

7. The viscount has not found a home yet and he regrets leaving his fine palace.

8. If your exhaust pipe rusts you just have to shrug and accept it.

9. Such a display could be either grand or rather vulgar.

10. Give the dog a bone and give him a little water.

Origins***

The following words can be found in any English dictionary, but from which languages did they originate?

1. Pince nez	2. Cul de sac	3. Pro tempore
4. Mañana	5. Fait accompli	6. Allegro
7. Bona fide	8. Mufti	9. Nosh
10. Pagoda	11. Voodoo	12. Taboo
13. Ombudsman	14. Origami	15. Guru
16. Kismet	17. Pundit	18. Quisling
19. Swastika	20. Halcyon	21. Habeas corpus
22. Marathon	23. Colossal	24. Vigilante

Slang Words*

In Cockney rhyming slang, the rhyming part is often omitted. For example, titfer (tit for tat, in full) is hat, and plates (plates of meat) are feet. Can you join each of the words in the first column to its rhyming part in the second column, and find its meaning in the third column? For example, apples (from the first column) and pears (from the second column) means stairs (from the third column).

WHISTLE	VARDEN	WIFE
TROUBLE	ROOTS	TEA
ROSIE	PLATE	SUIT
PIG'S	LEE	STAIRS
DOLLY	HOOK	MONEY
DAISY	EAR	MATE
CHINA	AND STRIFE	LOOK
BUTCHER'S	AND HONEY	GARDEN
BEES	AND PEARS	BOOTS
APPLES	AND FLUTE	BEER

English Spoken Here**

Below are some English words and phrases. Can you give the French equivalent? They are probably more familiar than the English.

1. According to the menu
2. With reference to
3. Trinket
4. Enjoy your meal
5. A witty comment
6. Miscellaneous objects
7. Complete freedom
8. That's life!
9. Exclusive group
10. Announcer at a revue
11. Habitual flirt
12. The best people
13. First performance
14. Social blunder
15. Style
16. Medley or mixture
17. Sharp, stinging
18. Powerful exhibition of skill
19. With regard to
20. Grand gesture

Down Under**

Australians speak English, but the English they speak isn't always exactly the same English as the English speak. When you are Down Under you may meet a banana bender and you will find he's got nothing to do with bananas: he just happens to come from Queensland. And if his first words to you are **'Don't come the raw prawn!'** he's not talking about uncooked shrimps, he is simply saying **'You can't fool me!'**

To find out if you would be fooled by an Australian speaking Australian, take a look at this list of Down Under English words and see how many you can match with the British equivalent in the second column.

Aussie 12	1 Sweets
Bathers	2 Mate
Billabong	3 Countryside
Bowser	4 Australian wild dog
Bush (the) 3	5 Sheep
Cobber 2	6 Baby kangaroo
Didgeridoo	7 Pupil on sheep/cattle station
Dingo 4	8 Bundle of belongings
Dinkum	9 Postman
Duds	10 Small wallaby
Goanna	11 Idiot
Good on you	12 Australia/Australian
Grazier	13 Petrol Pump
Gum tree	14 Suitcase
Jackeroo	15 Shark
Joey	16 Farmer
Jumbuck	17 Well done!
Lollies	18 Girl/woman
Milk bar	19 Eucalyptus tree
Moke	20 Lizard
Noah's ark	21 Pond
Nong	22 Swimming costume
Paddy melon	23 Trumpet
Pommy	24 Honest
Port	25 Englishman/woman
Postie	26 Horse
Sheila	27 Best clothes
Swag	28 Dairy & general grocery shop

PICTURE PUZZLES

SECTION ONE

Spot the Difference 1. Shop!*

This puzzle features two seemingly identical pictures, A and B. Whereas, in fact, picture B contains a dozen distinct differences. Can you spot them?

Maze 1 *

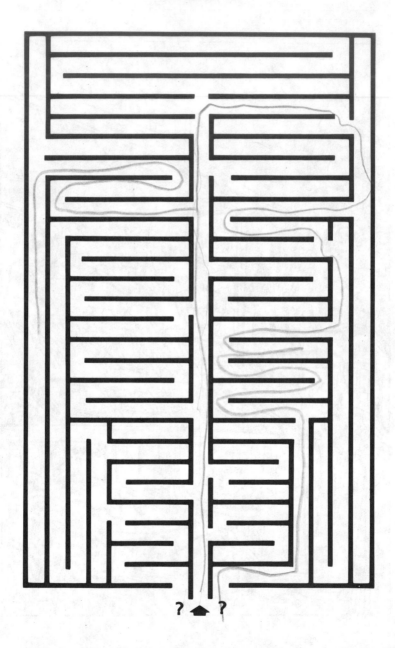

Spot the Mistake 1. Bonjour!*

'I do not mind lying, but I hate inaccuracy,' said Samuel Butler, and the truth is that in the following two drawings there may be one or two (or even three) inaccuracies. The Eiffel Tower sets the scene in France. Can you spot them?

Spot the Mistake 2. Cor Blimey!*

Something to shout about the day after the Coronation.

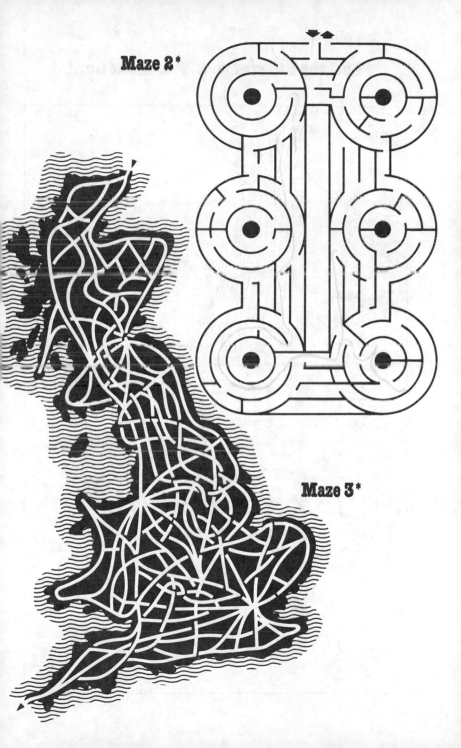

Maze 2*

Maze 3*

Spot the Difference 2. Fun in the Sun*

Picture B contains a dozen differences from picture A. Can you spot them?

NUMBER PUZZLES

Twenty Questions**

Here's a quick quiz in which all the questions have something to do with numbers. Otherwise the questions have nothing in common, they range from literary subjects, through films to baked beans! However, in order to jog your memory each question has four possible answers from which you have to choose the right one.

1. Is 'Number 10' –
   (a) the name of a make of cigarette?
   (b) the name of an expensive perfume?
   (c) the address of the British Prime Minister? ✓
   (d) the name of a secret society?

2. Is a '747' –
   (a) a kind of germ?
   (b) a kind of shotgun?
   (c) a kind of bomb?
   (d) a kind of aeroplane? ✓

3. Who wrote **The Thirty-nine Steps?** Was it –
   (a) Agatha Christie? ✓
   (b) Arthur Conan Doyle?
   (c) John Buchan?
   (d) John Galsworthy?

4. **4,406 feet** represents the height of which famous mountain –
   (a) Ben Nevis? ✓
   (b) Mont Blanc?
   (c) Mount Everest?
   (d) Mount Pico?

5. Who boasts about having **'57 Varieties'**? Is it –
   (a) Rolls-Royce who make motor cars?
   (b) Rowntrees who make sweets?
   (c) Heinz who make tinned foods? ✓
   (d) Waddingtons who make games?

6. Who wrote a novel called **1984**? Was it –
   (a) George Washington?
   (b) George Orwell?
   (c) George Brown?
   (d) George III?

7. What is or was the only coin in the world with **7 sides**? Is it, or was it –
   (a) the old French 10 franc piece?
   (b) the new British 20p piece?
   (c) the German Deutschmark?
   (d) the British 50p piece?

8. If you multiply **9** by **99** and multiply the result by **999** what do you get. Is it –

   (a) 999,999?
   (b) 890,109?
   (c) 9,999,999?
   (d) 4,765,220?

9. What is or was **2001**? Is it or was it –
   (a) the name of a new brand of toothpaste?
   (b) the name of a famous railway train?
   (c) the name of a well-known shoe polish?
   (d) the name of a science-fiction novel and film?

10. Who created **Special Agent 007**? Was it –
   (a) John Le Carré?
   (b) John Le Mesurier?
   (c) Ian Fleming?
   (d) Ian Carmichael?

11. Which was the first of the **Seven Wonders of the World**. Was it –
   (a) The Pyramids of Egypt?
   (b) The Taj Mahal?
   (c) The Grand Canyon?
   (d) The Eiffel Tower?

12. Were the **Seven Samurai** –
   (a) Indian temples?

(b) Chinese Sweets?
(c) African weapons?
(d) Japanese Warriors? ✓

13. In the Bible story, to whom did God give the **Ten Commandments** –
    (a) Solomon?
    (b) David?
    (c) Jesus?
    (d) Moses? ✓

14. **2.540 centimetres** is the same as –
    (a) ¼ inch?
    (b) 1 inch? ✓
    (c) 6 inches?
    (d) 2 feet?

15. What was the **R101**? Was it –
    (a) a type of submarine?
    (b) a type of airship? ✓
    (c) a type of steam engine?
    (d) a type of motor cycle?

16. Who wrote the book **Around the World in Eighty Days** from which the film was made? Was it –
    (a) H.G. Wells? ✓
    (b) Jules Verne?
    (c) Hammond Innes?
    (d) Georges Simenon?

17. According to the song, how many trombones were there in the big parade –
    (a) 2?
    (b) 51?
    (c) 76? ✓
    (d) 110?

18. If you multiply **2** times **2** times **2** times **2** times **2** times **2** times **2** times **2** times **2** times **2**, what do you get? Is it –
    (a) 2,222,222?
    (b) 2,000?
    (c) 864?
    (d) 1,024? ✓

19. With what game do you associate the phrases '**Legs 11**', '**All the fours, 44**' and '**On its own, number 1**'? Is it –
  (a) Cricket?
  (b) Bingo?
  (c) Roulette?
  (d) Bowls?

20. 8.047 kilometres are the same as –
  (a) 10 miles?
  (b) 8 miles?
  (c) 5 miles?
  (d) 1 mile?

What Next**

In this series of numbers, what number comes next:

$$1 \ 2 \ 3 \ 4 \ 5 \ 6 \ 7 \ 8 - ?$$

Did you say 9? Quite right. Well done. Let's make it a little tougher now. In this series, what comes next:

  a. 3 3 4 4 5 5 6 6 ?
  b. T T T F F S S E N ?
  c. 3 4 6 7 9 10 12 13 15 ?
  d. 1 9 1 4 1 9 1 8 1 9 3 9 1 9 4 5 ?
  e. 99 86 83 70 67 54 51 38 35 ?
  f. O T T F F S S E N T ?
  g. 10 15 13 18 16 21 19 24 22 27 ?
  h. 4445 7 89512 56734 42 89612 57 90 – ?

Pick a Number**

1. In Europe a **BILLION** equals a million times a million: 1,000,000,000,000. In America a billion's rather different. What does the American billion look like?

1,000,000,000?
1,000,000,000,000,000?
1,000,000,000,000,000,000,000?
1,000,000,000,000,000,000,000,000,000?

Pick a number

2. The Amazon is the world's longest river. How long is it?

2,899 miles?

4,195 miles?

6,800 miles?

12,631 miles?

Pick a number.

3. In the world today, there are roughly three babies born every second. In round figures, how many babies are born in a year?

60,000,000?

90,000,000?

120,000,000?

117,000,000,000?

Pick a number.

4. If a hippopotamus lived as long as it is possible for a hippopotamus to live, how old would the hippo be when he died?

10?

20?

40?

100?

Pick a number.

5. English is the second most spoken language in the world. How many people speak it?

291,000,000?

500,000,000?

994,000,000?

12,872,000,000?

Pick a number.

6. There are approximately two and a half centimetres in an inch, how many kilometres are there in a mile?

0.8?

1.6093?

2?

2.9802?

Pick a number

7. There are several theories about how the earth was formed but how old is it reckoned to be?

4,700,000,000 years?

4,700,000,000,000 years?

4,700,000,000,000,000 years?

4,700,000,000,000,000,000 years?

Pick a number.

8. If the capacity of a bus is around 50 cubic metres, what would you expect the capacity of a village church to be?

$100 \, m^3$?

$1,000 \, m^3$?

$10,000 \, m^3$?

$100,000 \, m^3$?

Pick a number.

9. A European **trillion** equals a million times a billion, so what does a European trillion look like?

1,000,000,000,000?

1,000,000,000,000,000?

1,000,000,000,000,000,000?

1,000,000,000,000,000,000,000?

Pick a number.

10. The tallest tree in Britain is a Grand Fir at Leighton Park in Gwent (Wales). How tall is it?

20 m?

38 m?

56 m?

72 m?

Pick a number.

Punch and Judy**

If you add the age of Punch to the age of Judy you get a combined age of 91 years. Punch is now twice as old as Judy was when he was as old as she is now. How old are Punch and Judy?

Monday to Friday**

Lady Agatha, when asked her age, replied that she was 35 years old, not counting Saturdays and Sundays. What was her real age?

AD/BC*

A man was born in the year 50 BC. How old was he on his birthday in 50AD?

Next Please**

In each of these series what should the next number be?

1. 31 28 31 30 —

2. 3 6 12 24 — *44*

3. 1 8 3 7 1 9 0 — *0*

4. 2 3 5 9 17 33 — *65*

5. 5 5 25 8 8 64 3 3 — *9*

6. 1 12 1 1 1 2 1 3 —

7. 1 6 2 7 3 8 4 — *9*

8. 940 839 738 637 — *536*

9. 4 8 32 512 131072 —

10. 111.11111 125 142.85714 166.66666 200 —

Big Shot*

Johnny, Willy and Bobby were fishing by the river, when suddenly someone on the other bank fired a gun. Johnny saw the smoke rising from the gun, Willy saw the bullet hit the water with a splash, and Bobby heard the gun go off with a loud bang. Which of the three boys knew about the shot first?

Now What?*

What should come next in this series? And why?

½ 1 2 5 10 20 50 1 5 10

How Much**

How much money would I have originally had in my wallet, if in spending one-fifth and then one-fifth of what remained, I altogether spent £36.00 somewhere?

Where There's a Will***

Mr Brown died recently, and in his will left just over £8,000 to be divided between his widow, his 5 sons, and 4 daughters. He stipulated that every son should receive three times as much as a daughter, and that every daughter should receive twice as much as their mother. If the precise amount left by the man was £8,000.07 how much did the widow receive?

Not so Silly Willy***

At the beginning of January little Willie told his parents that he had decided to save all his pocket money. He knew that he had been spending far too much and he realised that the time had come to put by some of the money his parents gave him for a rainy day. This was his plan:

On the first day of the month he wanted to save 1 penny.

On the second day of the month he wanted to save twice as much, two pennies.

On the third day of the month he wanted to save twice as much again, 4 pennies.

On the fourth day of the month he wanted to save twice as much again, 8 pennies.

On the fifth day he wanted to save twice as much again, 16 pennies.

And so he went on right through the month, each day saving twice as much as he'd saved the day before. Little Willie's parents, being sensible people, decided to encourage his thrift and gave him all the money he needed.

How much had little Willie managed to save by the last day of January?

Drink Up*

Two fathers and two sons went into an hotel to have a drink. The bill came to a total of £3. They each spent the same amount. How much did they pay?

The Lost Note**

Three men went into an hotel and were told that only one room was available and that it would cost £30 for the night. They each paid £10 and went to the room. Later that evening the receptionist realised that she had made an error and had overcharged the men £5. She asked one of the other hotel staff to return the £5 to the men. Unfortunately, this employee was none too honest. He realised that, since £5 is not easily divisible by 3, he would keep £2 and return £3 to the men so that each would get back £1. Each man therefore only paid £9, which totals £27 for the room. Add to that the £2 the employee kept, and the total is only £29.

What happened to the missing £1? Who had it? Where did it go?

Share Out**

You have three boys, Alex, Bobby and Colin. Divide 4,700 pennies among the three boys so that Alex gets 1,000 more pennies than Bobby, and Bobby receives 800 pennies more than Colin. How many pennies does each boy receive?

Bow and Arrow*

A bow and arrow cost £21. The bow costs £20 more than the arrow.
What is the price of each?

The Pools Winner***

Lucky had a win on the pools. On the day he collected his winnings he spent 95p. The next day he spent £1.90. The next day £2.85. The day after that £3.80, and so on, each day spending 95p more than on the previous day until finally he spent the last £190 of his winnings buying drinks for all his friends in the local pub.
What did Lucky's total winnings amount to?

WHAT TIME IS IT
WHEN THE CLOCK
STRIKES THIRTEEN?

TIME TO GET A NEW
CLOCK.

Auntie Nellie***

Auntie Nellie decided to leave £1,000 amongst her 5 nieces, but her last will and testament specified that the girls had to divide the money according to their ages, so that each niece received £20 more than the next niece younger to her.

How much did the youngest of the five nieces receive?

See a Man About a Dog**

A farmer bought a sheepdog, only to find that it was frightened of sheep. Fortunately for him some American tourists visited his farm and fell in love with the animal. As they cared little about its sheepishness, he sold the dog to them for £35 and half as much as he gave for it. The tourists were happy with their purchase, and the farmer had made a profit of £10.50.

How much did the farmer originally pay for the dog?

A Pound of Apples*

Two market traders were selling apples. One was selling 30 apples for £1, whilst the other offered 20 apples for £1. One afternoon they were both called away, and each had 300 apples unsold. These they handed to a friend to sell at 50 for £2.

It will be seen that if they had sold their apples separately, they would have made £25, but when they were sold together, they fetched only £24.

So what has happened to the missing pound? Surely, 30 for £1 and 20 for £1 is the same as 50 for £2, isn't it?

Inflation***

During the 4 years of my membership, my annual subscriptions to the F.A.I.L. (the Federated Anti-Inflation League) totalled £120. In the second year the subscription was £3 more than in the first year; in the third it was £2 more than in the second; and in the fourth year £6 more than in the third.

How much was the subscription for each year?

Your Number's Up*

In a local do-it-yourself shop, my neighbour was quoted 12 pence for one, 24 pence for 50, and 36 pence for 144. He wanted 6.

What was he buying and how much did it cost him?

Muggers' Money***

Two English gentlemen, Mr Ascot and Mr Berkshire, with £100 and £48 respectively, having to perform a journey through a lonely part of the country, decided to travel together for purposes of company. As they were walking through a wood a gang of youths jumped out and threatened them. The gang leader was satisfied with taking twice as much from Mr Ascot as from Mr Berkshire and left to Mr Ascot three times as much as to Mr Berkshire.

How much was taken from each?

Long Time*

A woman wound up two watches. It turned out that one of them went two minutes per hour too slow, and the other went one minute per hour too fast. When she looked at them again, the faster one was exactly one hour ahead of the other.

How long had the watches been running.

On Strike**

If an ordinary striking clock was turned into a 24 hour clock, so that at midnight it struck 24 times, how many times would the clock strike in a full 24 hour day?

Long Hands**

On a clock with an hour hand and a minute hand of the same length and indistinguishable, if the clock were set going at noon, what would be the first time that it would be impossible, by reason of the similarity of the hands, to be certain of the correct time? To give an exact answer you may need to deal in fractions of a second.

Felines and Rodents**

If 6 cats can devour 6 rats in one-tenth of an hour, how many would it take to devour 100 rats in 6,000 seconds?

Stitches in Time**

If two stitchers can stitch two stitches in two seconds, how many stitches can six stitchers stitch in six seconds?

Timetable***

A man was in a great hurry to catch the 1.15 pm train from Liverpool Street, and it was already past 1 o'clock. In the distance he saw a church clock, and although he could not see the dial he could just distinguish that the two hands were exactly together, so he knew what the time must be.

What was the time?

Party Time***

At a late night party it appeared to the guests that the clock had stopped half way through the party because the hands appeared in exactly the same position as when the party began. In fact the hands had actually changed places. As the party began between 10 and 11 o'clock, what were the two times?

Digital Clock*

What should be the next number in the sequence?

1 2 5 9 5 8 1 2 5 9 5 9 1 3 ...

The 'magic' of the Magic Square lies in the fact that whichever way you add up the numbers in the square – vertically, horizontally or diagonally – you always get the same answer. In this square, for example, the answer is always 15:

```
8  1  6
3  5  7
4  9  2
```

Here is another square, where the total for each line adds up to 62:

23	10	9	20
12	17	18	15
16	13	14	19
11	22	21	8

In this third sixteen-number square, the total is 150:

45	32	31	42
34	39	40	37
38	35	36	41
33	44	43	30

This next magic square contains twenty-five numbers. They add up to 105 in each direction, and if you add the four corner squares to the square in the middle you get 105 yet again:

25	32	9	16	23
31	13	15	22	24
12	14	21	28	30
18	20	27	29	11
19	26	33	10	17

Quarter of a Century***

The square below contains the numbers 1 to 25, and as you will see, all the rows, columns and long diagonals add up to 65.

17	24	1	8	15
23	5	7	14	16
4	6	13	20	22
10	12	19	21	3
11	18	25	4	9

What you have to do is try and form a similar Magic Square, using all the numbers 1 to 25, but begin with the number 1 in the centre of your square. The rows, columns, and diagonals must all add up to 65.

Radioactive Problem***

Nuclear waste is always a problem. If too much radioactive material is put together it is liable to endanger any living object within quite a wide range. Some radioactive materials, such as uranium, are kept in canisters and are buried in the ground. The diagram below represents 9 such canisters, each with a number on the top to show the strength of the material contained within.

This particular group, however, is highly dangerous because if 3 canisters are in a row their total strength must not be more than thirty units. If you add up the rows you will see that in many cases the totals far exceed the recommended safety limit.

$$13 \quad 6 \quad 14$$
$$11 \quad 10 \quad 3$$
$$9 \quad 17 \quad 7$$

Can you rearrange the containers so that no single line (row, column or diagonal) adds up to more than thirty? Owing to the possible risk to your health, make sure you move the smallest number of containers you can.

Nine-a-side**

Lord Crabtree bought 28 bottles of wine, and not sure whether he could trust the butler, he placed the bottles in his cellar in a container, in such a way that he could count 9 bottles on each side, like this:

$$2 \quad 5 \quad 2$$
$$5 \qquad 5$$
$$2 \quad 5 \quad 2$$

Notwithstanding this precaution, the butler removed 4 bottles and rearranged the bottles so that the next time Lord Crabtree counted them there were still 9 bottles on each side. Delighted by his cunning, the butler removed a further 4 bottles on the following day, and again rearranged the bottles so as to count 9 bottles along each side. How did he do it?

Misplacement*

In the Magic Square below all the lines of four figures should add up to 34, whether read across, down or diagonally. By mistake, two numbers have been wrongly placed. Can you discover which two?

16	3	2	13
5	10	11	8
9	6	12	7
4	15	14	1

Amazing!**

Here is a remarkable magic square. Work out whether or not the rows, columns and diagonals all total the same, and what that total is. Then decide what is the special property of this particular square?

8818	1111	8188	1881
8181	1888	8811	1118
1811	8118	1181	8888
1188	8881	1818	8111

CALCULATOR PUZZLES

If mental arithmetic is not to your liking, you many prefer push button puzzles. For these calculating brainteasers are for you; all you need is a pocket calculator. The solutions are then at your fingertips.

Mini Quiz*

This is a quiz and calculation combined:

1. Multiply the year of the Battle of Waterloo by a score.
2. Multiply the answer by the number of days in May.
3. Divide the answer by the number of years in a decade.
4. Add one percent of an American billion.
5. Now subtract the date of the Battle of Trafalgar.
6. Divide the total by the number of years an octogenarian has lived.

What is the answer?

Talking Calculators*

Incredible as it may sound, pocket calculators have names. To find out the name of yours, press 317537 and turn the calculator upside down.

Now that you see your calculator can spell as well as calculate, what numbers would you need to spell out the following words? (REMEMBER that you have to press the numbers in reverse order, so that when you turn the calculator upside down the word will be spelt the right way.)

1. GIGGLE   2. SOIL   3. GOSH   4. HOLE
5. BELLS   6. GOBBLE   7. BOILS   8. BLESSES

The Percent Puzzle***

For the puzzle opposite you will need a paper and pencil as well as your calculator.

Begin at 0 then work out the percentage in the first box and write it down, then work out the next box and subtract that, and so on. If you are right, the answer at the end will be 0.

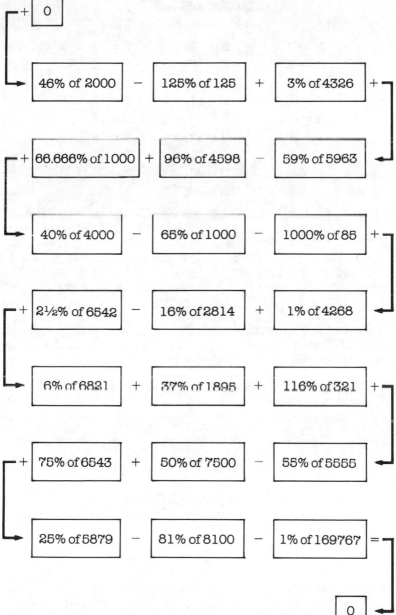

To the Letter**

To solve these problems you will need to use the following cipher:

A = 1	B = 2	C = 3
D = 4	E = 5	F = 6
G = 7	H = 8	I = 9
J = 10	K = 11	L = 12
M = 13	N = 14	O = 15
P = 16	Q = 17	R = 18
S = 19	T = 20	U = 21
V = 22	W = 23	X = 24
Y = 25	Z = 26	

Using this cipher you can put words into numbers. Using the list of words below, and working letter by letter, with your calculator, multiply the first letter by the second, divide by the third letter, add the fourth and subtract the fifth, and continue multiplying, dividing, adding, and subtracting each letter until you eventually reach the end of the word. Always follow the same order:

$$x \div + -$$

For example, if you were going to do the number code on the word **M O N D A Y**, it would be $13 \times 15 \div 14 + 4 - 1 \times 25$. Use the cipher to 'calculate' the following words.

1. WEDNESDAY   2. FRIDAY
3. SUNDAY   4. JANUARY
5. MARCH   6. APRIL
7. JUNE   8. SEPTEMBER
9. OCTOBER   10. YEAR

Dictionary Digits**

Here are some more calculator words. The answers to the following questions when entered on your calculator, if you turn the display upside down, will look very similar to letters of the alphabet and the answer should spell a whole word.

1. $15^2 - 124 \times 5$ will give you a distress signal.
2. $217 \times 121 - 8,550$ gives you something that goes with a pop.
3. $100,000 - 6,000 + 152 \times 4$ will do something to your mind.

4. The square root of 196 will give you a greeting.

5. .161616 ÷ 4 tells you what Santa Claus said when he fell down the chimney.

6. 44 x 70 will give you a musical instrument.

7. 12,570 + 0.75 x 16 ÷ 333 = an animal.

8. 52,043 ÷ 71 will give you a snakelike fish.

Common Factor*

Calculate the answers to these sums and work out what the calculations have in common.

1. 8 x 473	**2.** 9 x 351
3. 15 x 93	**4.** 21 x 87
5. 27 x 81	**6.** 35 x 41

Multiplication Digits***

The following sums use all the nine digits, 1 to 9, to make up the multiplications and the answers. Work out the digits before checking them on your calculator. In each case you will have to discover what the number is being multiplied by.

1.	**2.**	**3.**	**4.**
1963	198	1738	159
x ?	x ?	x ?	x ?
———	———	———	———

The Weigh In**

At a fruit stall on a market, 8 bananas, 7 apples and 3 grapefruit weigh as much as 3 apples, 6 bananas, and 6 grapefruit. If a banana weighs two-thirds as much as a grapefruit and a dozen apples weigh 3 kilograms, how much does a grapefruit weigh?

Add and Subtract**

These four odd-looking equations all have the same things missing – their plus and minus signs. See if you can put them to rights. Each one needs two plus signs and two minus signs arranged correctly in the spaces between the figures in order to make it work out. In the last one, you will also have to move two of the figures together to form one number.

(a) 5 4 3 2 1 = 5
(b) 2 2 3 4 5 = 0
(c) 5 3 1 3 5 = 5
(d) 1 2 3 4 5 6 = 10

999999?*

How could you write the number one hundred with six nines?

Drunkards**

A man can drink a barrel of beer in 20 days, but if his wife also drinks, they can finish the barrel in 14 days. How long would it take the wife to drink the barrel of beer alone?

Keep the Doctor Away*

They do say an apple a day keeps the doctor away, but they also say 'all things in moderation'. This was often said to young Benet, but children have to learn by experience, and the warning of 'Don't eat too many green apples' went unheeded.

So Benet ate two-thirds as many of those green apples as Aaron would have eaten if Aaron had eaten six more than half as many as Benet would have eaten if Benet had eaten three less than Aaron would have eaten.

How many apples does that make the cause of Benet's tummy-ache?

Tea-time*

A cup and saucer together weigh 12 ounces. The cup weighs twice as much as the saucer. How much does the saucer weigh?

Bookworm**

On a shelf is a 6-volume set of books standing side by side in order. Each cover on every volume is 3 millimetres thick, which is 6 millimetres back and front, and text which is 3 centimetres thick. A bookworm has eaten its way straight through the first page of volume 1 through to the last page of volume 6.

How far has the bookworm travelled?

Stick in the Mud*

One-ninth of a log was found stuck in mud, five-sixths was above water, and 2 feet of it was in the water. How long is the log?

Fishy Problem*

A fish's tail weighs nine pounds. Its head weighs as much as the tail and one-third of the body combined, and the body weighs as much as the head and tail combined. What does the whole fish weigh?

Number Scrabble***

Each of the letters below corresponds uniquely to a numerical digit. Find the correspondence to make this digit correct.

```
A L P H A B E T
+ L E T T E R S
-----------------
S C R A B B L E
-----------------
```

Baby Monkeys*

If a baby monkey weighs three-quarters of a baby monkey plus three quarters of a pound, how much does a baby monkey weigh?

Farm Fare*

A farmer, being asked what number of animals he kept on his farm, answered, 'They're all horses but two, all sheep but two, and all pigs but two.'
How many animals did he have in all?

Talking Turkey*

If a turkey weighs 10 kg and a half of its own weight, what does the turkey weigh?

What's the Difference?**

What is the difference between 4 square kilometres and 4 kilometres square?

Two Dozen**

Using just three digits, write out a simple addition sum that totals 24. The digits must all be the same, but they can't be 8!

Four Fives*

Use four fives to make 6½!

Sum Subtraction!***

Take 45 away from 45 and leave 45 as the remainder! If you think it can't be done, think again. Here's one way:

$$987654321 = 45$$
$$-123456789 = 45$$

$$864197532 = 45$$

Using the same system, can you find another way?

Ten Not Out*

Look at this carefully:

Now make TEN out of it by adding only five more lines.

Father and Son**

A son asked his father how old he was and this is the reply his father gave him: 'Your age is now one quarter of mine, but five years ago it was only one-fifth.' How old is the father?

Fowl-up**

Let's end with a really fowl problem! If a hen and a half lays an egg and a half in a day and a half, how many eggs will 6 hens lay in 7 days?

PICTURE PUZZLES

SECTION TWO

Spot the Difference 3. Departure Time

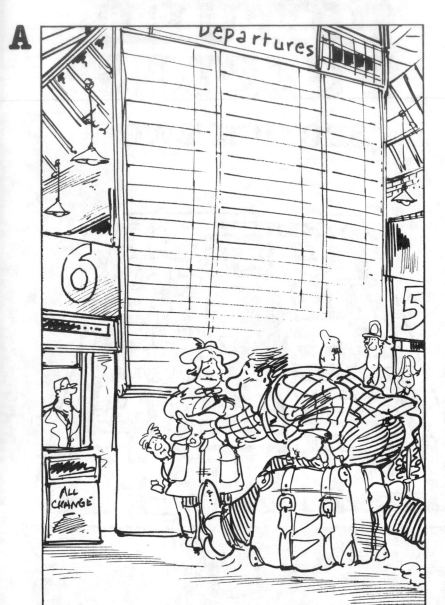

A and B are almost identical pictures but picture B has fourteen differences. Can you spot them?

Maze 4**

Spot the Mistake 3. Ex Libris**

What's wrong in this library?

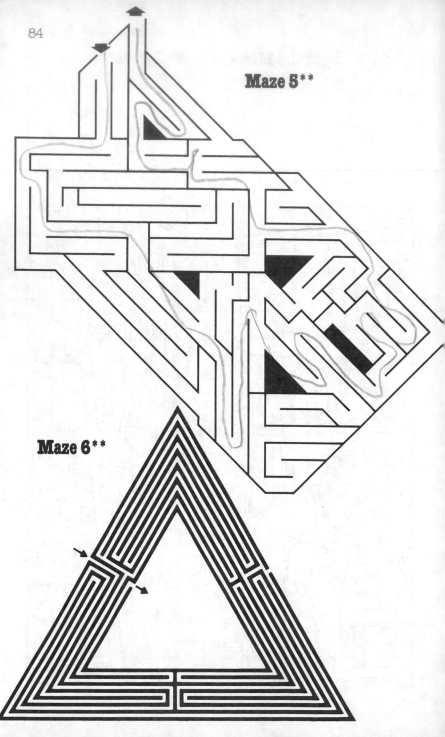

Maze 5**

Maze 6**

Maze 7

Maze 8

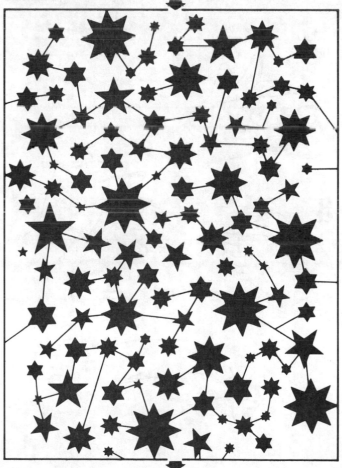

Shadow Shows**

In Victorian times shadow shows were a popular form of home entertainment. With the use of a lamp projected on a blank wall, and a skilled pair of hands, the shadows of a variety of people and creatures could be created. Here are some of the hand positions for casting interesting shadows. Can you say what the shadow would be in each case?

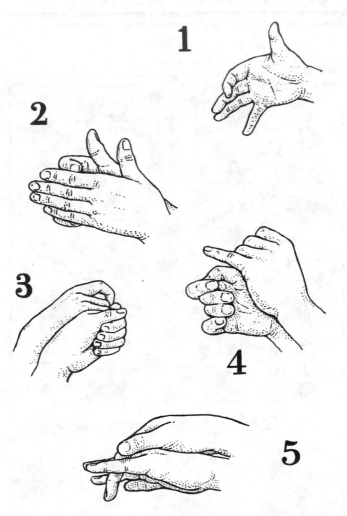

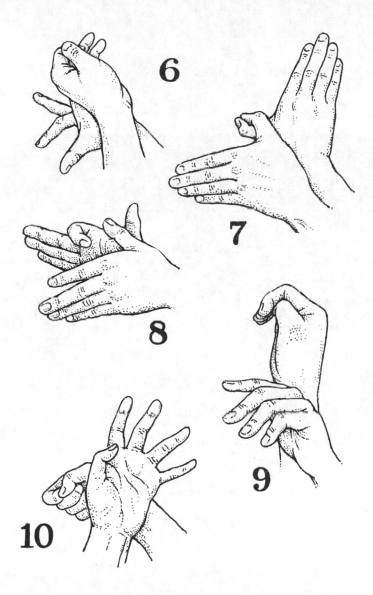

BRAINTEASERS
AND
MIND ENDERS

$$\frac{\begin{array}{r} 144 \\ \times \ 6 \end{array}}{864}$$

Value the Difference*

Is there any difference in value between six dozen dozen and a half dozen dozen? $864 - 72 = 792$

Family Problems**

A boy has as many sisters as he has brothers, but each of his sisters has twice as many brothers as she has sisters. How many boys and girls are there in the family? $(g - 3\ boys)$

Poor but Honest*

How many of these riddles can you answer?

1. Why must a dishonest man stay indoors?
2. Why is an honest friend like orange chips?
3. What men are above board in their movements?
4. Why is a false friend like your shadow?
5. What kind of vice is it that people dislike if they are ever so bad?
6. Who is the oldest lunatic on record?
7. Why did the moron throw all his nails away?
8. What is the height of folly?
9. Why is a blockhead deserving of promotion?
10. What are the most unsociable things in the world?
11. What is more to be admired than a promising young man?
12. What chasm often separates friends?
13. Where lies the path of duty?
14. What is the best way to keep loafers from standing on the street corner?
15. Why should you always remain calm when you encounter cannibals?

Brief Encounter*

Lady Constance met the Countess of Kensington in the laun-

derette. 'Don't I know you?' enquired Lady Constance.
'You certainly ought to,' replied the Countess.
'Your mother was my mother's only daughter.'
How are they related?   *MOTHER & DAUGHTER*

Four of a Kind**

It's no laughing matter to have to find a common English word of eight letters which contains four Gs. Try.   *GIGGLING*

Poetical Problem***

Curtail me thrice, I am a youth;
Behead me once, a snake;   *LADDER*
Complete, I'm often used, in truth,
When upward steps you take.

Who or what am I?

Easy**

The beginning of eternity,   *E*
The end of time and space,
The beginning of every end,
The end of every place.

What can be described in this way?

Which Way?***

You find yourself in the strange country of Everywhere and have lost your way. You could be in the town of Here or There. All the inhabitants of Here tell the truth, but the inhabitants of There always tell lies. As you walk down the street you see a man approaching and you know that he is either from Here or There. What one question would you ask him to find out where you are?

ARE WE IN HERE

Choral Conundrum?*

Add the bottom of a woman's dress to an insect and you will get a musical number sung by a church choir.

What is the word?

Cat-astrophe*

If three cunning cats can catch three masterful mice in three minutes, how many cunning cats could catch one hundred masterful mice in one hundred minutes?

Russian Riddle*

Solve the following puzzle in under 30 seconds.

Two Russians walk down a street in Moscow. One Russian is the father of the other Russian's son. How are they related?

Jumbled Letters*

Unscramble the following letters so that they spell just one word:

NETOUSDJORW

Aunts and Uncles**

A man and his sister were out walking together one Saturday morning. The man pointed across the street to a boy and said: 'That boy is my nephew.' The woman replied: 'He is not *my* nephew.' Can you explain this?

The Whole Lot*

How much dirt is there in a hole 3 metres deep and 1 metre square?

Revolutionary Conundrum*

Add a girl's name from a famous American battle to an ancient Roman garment, and what do you get?

False or True*

Some of these statements are true. Some are false. Can you spot the false ones?

1. Until 1957 it was illegal to go swimming in the State of New York on a Sunday.

2. Teddy bears were named after the American President Theodore Roosevelt.

3. In southern Italy tulips are not only grown because they are nice to look at, but also because they are considered a delicacy and are regularly eaten as part of a salad.

4. Typewriters were first developed to help the blind.

5. Benjamin Franklin invented the digital clock in 1777.

6. An earthworm can pull ten times its own weight.

7. Originally the yo-yo was a Filipino jungle weapon.

8. Cars were first started by ignition keys in 1949.

9. William Lee invented a knitting machine in 1589.

10. Indian ink actually comes from China.

11. The oldest account of a chimney describes one in Venice in 1347.

12. President Dwight Eisenhower was once North American Monopoly Champion.

13. Cleopatra was the product of six generations of brother/sister marriages.

14. Elephants cannot jump.

15. No mammal has poisonous glands.

16. A gorilla's brain weighs 10 lb.

17. The Romans used weasels to catch mice.

18. Only male nightingales sing.

19. The Emperor Napoleon was an alcoholic.

20. Ovid wrote a book about cosmetics.

21. It is recorded that Louis XIII of France was bled forty-seven times in one month.

22. Queen Marie Antoinette of France and the actress Jayne Mansfield had identical bust measurements.

23. 'School' is derived from the Greek word Skhole which means 'leisure'.

24. Six different dialects are spoken in India.

25. During their studies medical students increase their vocabulary by 10,000 words.

ALL SHAPES AND SIZES

Three Dimensional Shapes**

Here are some patterns for solid forms. Which pattern would make up which figure?

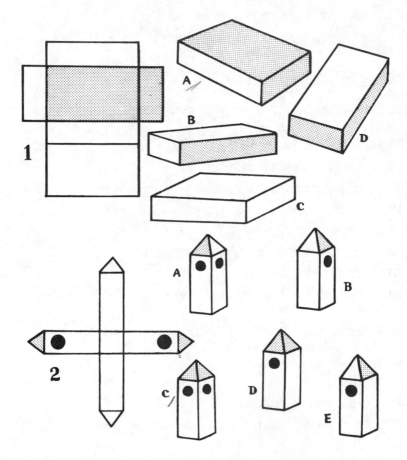

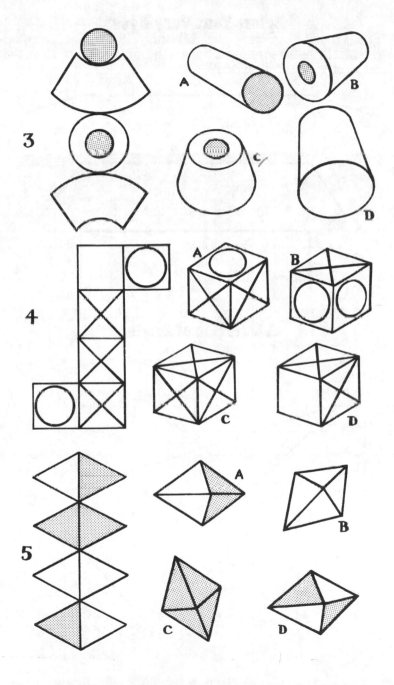

Before Your Very Eyes*

Try out these geometric puzzlers: but no cheating with a ruler!
Which of these three straight lines is the longest: the top one, the
middle one or the bottom one?

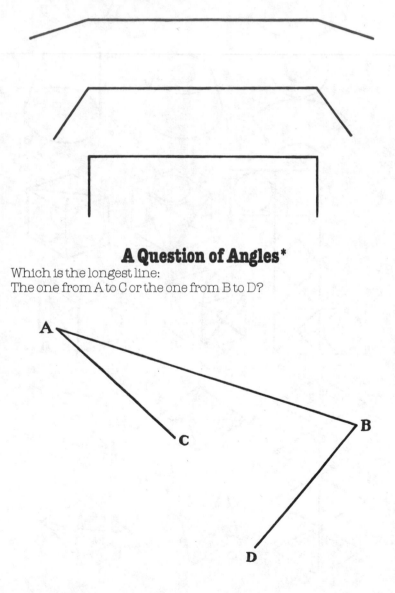

A Question of Angles*

Which is the longest line:
The one from A to C or the one from B to D?

WHAT QUESTION CAN
NEVER BE ANSWERED 'YES'?

'ARE YOU ASLEEP?'

The Distance*

Is B nearer to A
or nearer to C.

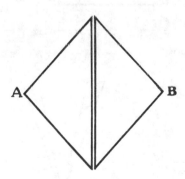

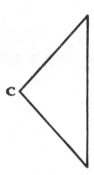

A Matter of Size**

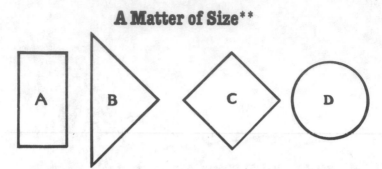

Above are 4 fields. Which is the largest and which the smallest?

Curious Cube**

From which angle are we looking at this cube? Is it viewed from above or from below? Is the line across the corner of the cube straight or bent?

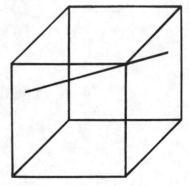

Right Angles*

Which is the largest angle: Angle A or angle B?

Key to the Problem**

Here are six bunches of keys. On each key ring only TWO keys are identical, the rest are different. Can you say which is a pair in each case?

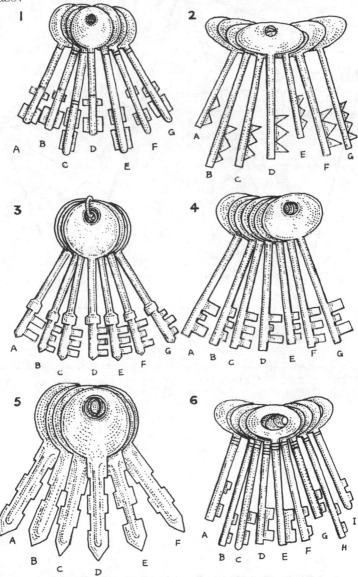

Triangular Terror*
How many triangles are there in the figure below?

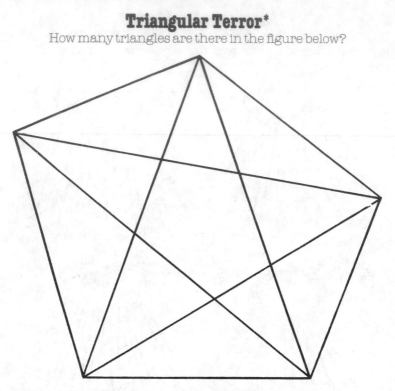

Mystery of the Sphinx***
Can you solve the mystery of the Sphinx? All you have to do is divide the figure into 4 equal parts, each one being a miniature of the Sphinx shape but they can be placed upside down or sideways. It is possible!

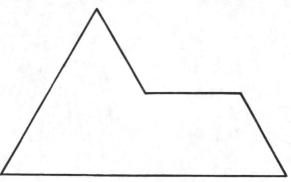

All Square*

Cut this figure into 4 pieces, each of the same size and shape, that will fit together and form a perfect square.

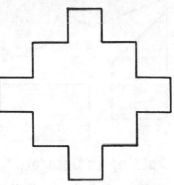

Square and Triangle**

Take a square piece of paper and fold it so as to form the largest possible equilateral triangle. The triangle in which the sides are the same length as those of the square, as shown in the diagram, will *not* be the largest possible. No markings or measurements may be made except by the creases themselves.

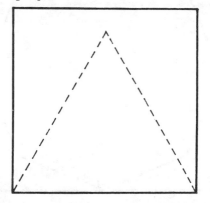

Paper Letter**

Cut out the shapes below from a piece of paper or card. Put them together to form a certain letter of the alphabet. Which letter is it?

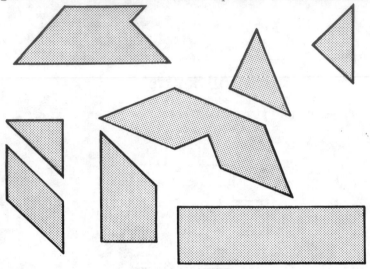

Folding an Octagon**

Can you cut a regular octagon from a square piece of paper without using compasses or ruler or anything but scissors? You can fold the paper so as to make creases.

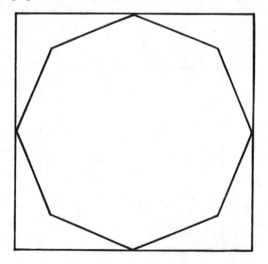

Biggest Hole in the World***

This puzzle sounds impossible, but it isn't! All you need is a sheet of ordinary writing paper and a pair of scissors. What you have to do is cut a hole in the paper large enough for you to climb through! When you have completed the puzzle you should have a hole large enough for you to place the paper over your head, pass it over your body, and step through it without tearing it. It can be done, honestly!

Pinhole Puzzle*

Take two pieces of card. A visiting card or playing card will do. In one of the cards prick three very small holes with the point of a pin. These must be very close together so that they do not cover an area greater than the pupil of the eye. In the second piece of card prick one single pin hole. Now, hold the card with the three pinholes as close to your eye as possible, and the other card with one pinhole about 2 or 3 inches (5 cm) away from the first. On looking through the first card, what appears to happen to the second?

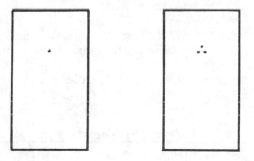

Quick Quiz*

1. Folk is spelt F.O.L.K. *not* F.O.K.E. Joke is spelt J.O.K.E. *not* J.O.L.K. How do you spell the white of an egg?

2. How many grooves are there on a gramophone record that revolves at 45 r.p.m.? And how many are there on one that revolves at 33⅓ r.p.m.?

3. Mr Broke the Banker has two coins in his left-hand pocket. Together they add up to 60p. One of them is not a 50p piece, so what are the two coins?

4. What do you find right in the middle of Glasgow?

5. What one word in the Oxford English Dictionary do people from Chicago always pronounce incorrectly?

6. In a leap year, how many months have 28 days?

7. What do you get if you add 2 to 200 four times?

8. If I have 467 large conkers and 193 small conkers in my prize conker collection and I take away all but a dozen of them, how many will I have left?

9. In the whole history of the world, have New Year's Eve and New Year's Day ever fallen in the same year?

10. I own something round and flat and black and shiny with a small hole right in the middle of it. Is this a record?

One Number*

If you add 1,000 to a certain whole number, the result will be actually more than if you multiplied that number by 1,000! What's the number?

Unlucky Thirteen*

Here are thirteen letters:

J F M A M R J J A S O N D

One of them doesn't belong to the series. Which one?

Lewis Carroll's Puzzles**

The creator of Alice in Wonderland and Through the Looking Glass was also an enthusiastic puzzler. Here are five of his favourite brainteasers.

1. John gave his brother James a box:
   About it there were many locks.
   James woke and said it gave him pain;
   So gave it back to John again.
   The box was not with lid supplied
   Yet caused two lids to open wide:
   And all these locks had never a key
   What kind of box, then, could it be?

2. Three sisters at breakfast were feeding the cat.
   The first gave it sole, Puss was grateful for that:
   The next gave it salmon, which Puss thought a treat:
   The third gave it herring, which Puss wouldn't eat.

   Explain the conduct of the cat.

3. When the King found that his money was nearly all gone, and that he really must live more economically, he decided on sending away most of his Wise Men. There were some hundreds of them, all very fine old men, and magnificently dressed in green velvet gowns with gold buttons. If they had a fault, it was that they always contradicted one another when he asked for their advice, and they certainly ate and drank enormously. So, on the whole, he was rather glad to get rid of them. But there was an old law, which he did not dare to disobey, which said that there must always be:

   Seven blind of both eyes:
   Ten blind of one eye:
   Five that see with both eyes:
   Nine that see with one eye.

   Query: How many did he keep?

4. Below are three pairs of statements. What conclusion can you draw from each of the pairs? For example, if you were told 'No professors are ignorant' and 'All ignorant people are vain', the

conclusion you would draw would be that 'No professors are vain.' Now try these.

> **1.** No doctors are enthusiastic.
> You are enthusiastic.

> **2.** Dictionaries are useful.
> Useful books are valuable.

> **3.** No misers are unselfish.
> None but misers save bottle tops.

5. If seventy percent of people in an old folks home have lost an eye, seventy-five percent have lost an ear, eighty percent have lost an arm, and eighty-five percent a leg – what percentage at least must have lost all four?

The Bridge Problem***

Four ladies – Avril, Betty, Connie and Davina – and three men – Ernest, Frank, and George – all play bridge together. It is a card game for four players.

1. One evening they played four bridge games in which the partners were:
Avril and Ernest versus Betty and Frank
Avril and George versus Davina and Frank
Betty and Connie versus Frank and George
Connie and Ernest versus Davina and George

2. No more than one married couple ever play in the same game.

3. The members of each married couple are never partners in a game.

4. The men and women consist of three married couples and a widow.

Who is the widow?

Death by Drowning***

Anthony, Bob and Charles were questioned by a detective about Dolly's death by drowning.

1. Anthony said: If it was murder, Bob did it.

2. Bob said: If it was murder, I did not do it.
3. Charles said: If it was not murder, it was suicide.
4. The detective said truthfully: If just one of these three men lied it was suicide.

How did Dolly die? Was it accident, suicide or murder?

Marriage Lines**

Messrs Lagan, Foyle, Bann and Erne are neighbours. Three of them are married. One of the four is bald, one redheaded and one dark-haired.

Mr Erne isn't redheaded, nor is he dark-haired, but is married.
Mr Lagan isn't bald nor is he fairhaired, but is single.
Mrs Bann is blonde but her husband is neither dark-haired nor bald.
Mr Foyle doesn't have either fair or dark hair.
Mr Erne's wife is dark-haired while the bald-headed man has a redheaded wife.

With this set of facts, can you work out the following:

1. **Whose wife is a redhead?** FOYLE
2. **What colour hair has the single man?** DARK
3. **Mrs Foyle's husband has which hair colour?** BALD

Mad Cap***

The King of Sellonica needed a man of great courage and wisdom for a very important mission. Unable to decide which of his three best knights should do the job, he called them to him and had them blindfolded. Then he placed a cap on the head of each one and said:

'Each of you now wears either a black or a white cap. When the blindfolds are removed, I want you to raise your hand as soon as you see a black cap. Drop your hand as soon as you know the colour of your own cap.'

The blindfolds were removed, and all the knights raised their hands immediately, for the wily old man had placed a black cap on each knight's head. After a few minutes one courtier dropped his hand and said:

'My cap is black.'

By what logical reasoning had he reached that conclusion?

A Hit or a Miss**

The teacher asked Billy a question:

'If a certain missile will hit its target one out of four times, and four such missiles are fired at one target, then what is the probability that the target will be hit?'

'That's simple,' replied Billy, 'it's a certainty one missile will hit the target.' Was he right?

One Word*

There is one everyday English word which, when printed in capital letters, reads exactly the same upside down as it does the right way up. What's the word?

A Time Teaser**

When you see the reflection of a clock in a mirror and the time appears to be 2.30, what time is it really?

Letters Salad*

Here are five rows of letters:

```
I C A C
I C A B
I C A J
I C A U
I C A Z
```

One of the rows doesn't belong to the series. Which one?

What's Hot*

It burns no coal, no oil, no gas and it has no need of electricity, and yet it is far hotter than all the ovens and fires and blast furnaces in the United States when they are heated to capacity. What is it?

Alarming*

If on the last day of February 1980 – and remember, 1980 was a leap year – you had gone to bed at seven o'clock, having set your alarm clock to wake you up at 8.15 a.m. how much sleep would you have got?

Twin Twister*

Jack and Jill were born on the same day in the same year and are the children of the same parents – and yet they are not twins. How come?

Train Trial*

A boy is on a train, which is travelling at 60 miles per hour. He jumps straight up in the air 3 feet. Where does he land?

WHAT SHIP HAS TWO MATES BUT NO CAPTAIN ?

COURTSHIP.

Charades**

Here is a Victorian charade puzzle. Like the game of charades, the versified clues provide the separate syllables of a word, and then finally the complete word. Your task is to identify the mystery word.

> In the early spring, one silent night,
> The bold Sir Wilfred strayed
> Beneath his lady's lattice bright,
> To sing a serenade.
> He sat him down upon my *first*
> And there his loving lay rehearsed.
>
> A silvery mist hung o'er the scene
> Where thus he breathed his vows;
> And dewdrops gemmed the herbage green,
> And decked the budding boughs.
> But ah! Sir Wilfred should have reckoned
> The grass was sure to be my *second*.
>
> Next morn he did his foot page call,
> And bade at once repair
> To gay Lord Guthlac's festival hall,
> And him this message bear:
> 'Tell hib I'b ill, upod by soul!
> And can't todight attend by *whole*!'

Letter by Letter***

Here are 9 words which have something important in common. What is it?

1. Brandy
2. Chastens
3. Craters
4. Grangers
5. Pirated
6. Scampi
7. Stores
8. Swingers
9. Tramps

That's Cricket**

Two bowlers during the season have each taken 28 wickets for 60 runs. One bowler in the next match takes 4 wickets for 36 runs, and the other takes 1 wicket for 27 runs.

Which now has the best average?

Plural Puzzle***

Can you supply the plural for each of these words?

1. Daughter-in-law
2. Attorney general
3. Brigadier general
4. Judge advocate
5. Chargé d'affaires
6. Potato
7. Notary public
8. Law merchant
9. Opus
10. Pelvis
11. Sergeant major
12. Teaspoonful
13. Piccolo
14. Table d'hôte
15. Court martial
16. Paymaster general
17. Mister
18. Madam
19. Crisis
20. Man of war
21. Lieutenant colonel
22. Bandit
23. Cannon
24. Phenomenon
25. Aviatrix
26. Manservant
27. Oboe
28. Ox
29. Valet de chambre
30. Datum

Special Feature***

Here is a limerick with a very special feature. What is it?

When an expert burlesque queen named Maizy,
Stripping velvet, became very lazy.
She would quickly exhibit
Just one jewelled explicit,
Gliding off from the jokesters like crazy.

Underground Stations*

Each of a dozen well known London Underground Stations has had part of its name removed and the missing part replaced by a clue to it in brackets. How many of the dozen can you identify?

1. (compass point) minster
2. Le(frozen water)ster Square
3. E(you and me)ton
4. (conqueror)ia
5. B(be without) friars
6. (Draw along)er Hill
7. C(running very fast) Cross
8. (cook by dry heat) r Street
9. King(lean unsteadily)
10. (inexperienced) Park
11. (leave in difficulties or run aground)
12. (big animal) and (fortress)

Beauty Queens***

Of the three finalists in the bathing beauty contest, Amelia is older than the redhead, but younger than the hairdresser. Bernice is younger than the blonde, whilst Caroline is older than the brunette. The typist is the receptionist's younger sister. Can you give the hair colouring and profession of each girl in order of age?

Find the Number**

Find a four digit number which satisfies each of the three following conditions:
1. The last digit is twice the first digit.
2. The third digit is twice the second digit.
3. The sum of the first and last digits is twice the third digit.

All in the Family**

A man has three sons, and each of his sons has three sons. Using this information, answer the following questions.

1. How many pairs of cousins are there?
2. How many pairs of father and son?
3. How many pairs of brothers?
4. How many pairs of uncle and nephew?
5. How many pairs of grandfather and grandson?
6. How many people are there in the group?

Remember that one man may be in any number of pairs. He and his father are one pair, the same man and his son are another pair.

Liquid Refreshment*

If you were given a 5-pint container and a 3-pint container, how could you measure out 1 pint of liquid?
You have an unlimited supply of liquid with which to do this puzzle.

PICTURE PUZZLES
SECTION THREE

Spot the Difference 4. School's Out***

Can you spot twelve distinct differences on picture B compared with picture A?

Spot the Mistake 4. Victorian Parlour***

Here is a typical parlour the day after Prince Albert's death except that some things are out of place. Which are they?

Maze 9***

Maze 10***

Spot the Mistake 5. Pharaoh's Folly***

This artist's impression of Pharaoh's tomb is a little too free. Can you spot the inaccuracies?

Spot the Difference 5. Waiter***

Can you spot twelve distinct differences on picture B compared with picture A?

MATCHSTICK PUZZLES

See if you can strike it lucky by solving all these unmatchable puzzles, for which you will need nothing more than a box of matches.

Triangular Trouble*

1. Take 9 matches and lay them out in 3 triangles:

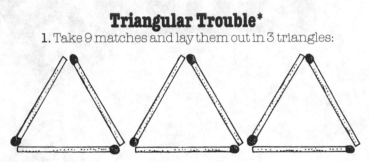

Now see if you can make 5 triangles by moving just 3 of the matches.

2. Lay down six matches to make this pattern:

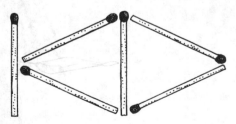

Move 3 of these matches to make 8 equilateral triangles.

3. With 5 matches see if you can make 2 triangles.

4. Take 9 matches and with them make 5 triangles.

5. Take sixteen matches and make up this pattern:

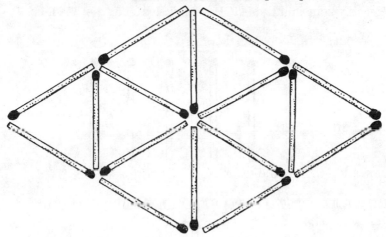

Remove 4 matches and leave just 4 triangles.

Matcho**

Remove four of the matches in this pattern and leave nine squares:

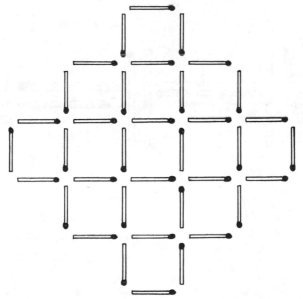

MatheMATCHics*

Here are some matheMATCHical puzzles using matchsticks:

1. Set out six matches like this:

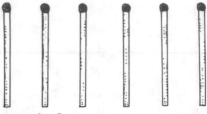

Now add 5 more to make 9.

2. Move just 1 match to make this Roman sum work:

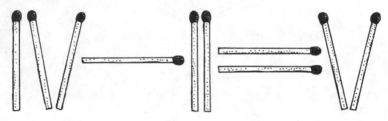

3. Make this sum correct by adding just 1 match:

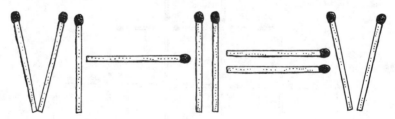

4. Move 2 matches to make this sum correct:

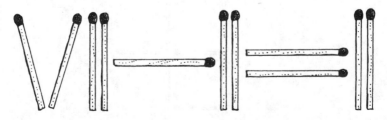

5. Remove 3 matches to make this sum correct:

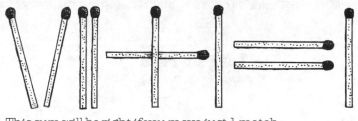

6. This sum will be right if you move just 1 match.

7. Make this sum correct without moving any matches:

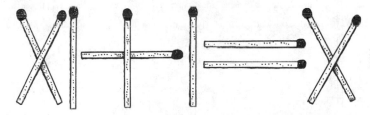

Untouchables***

This puzzle will really set you thinking. Take six matches and arrange them on the table in such a way that each match is touching the other five. It can be done!

All You Need*

With 16 matches create 4 squares like this:

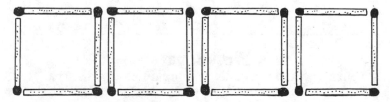

Now take away 4 of the matches, move 3 of the remaining ones and see if you can end up with what it is that makes the world go round.

Long Division**
With 16 matches form a figure like this:

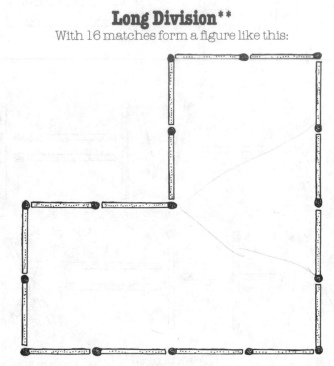

Now add 8 more matches and divide the shape into 4 equal parts.

First Square*
This puzzle should not cause you too much trouble. Take the 6 lowest dominoes in the set, the 0/0, the 0/1, the 0/2, the 1/1, the 1/2

and the 2/2, and arrange them in a square so that all the joins match in number. The shape of the square should be just like this one:

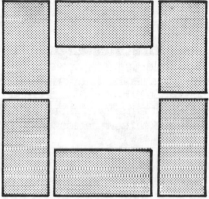

Second Square**

Take the same six dominoes as you used in the First Square, the 0/0, the 0/1, the 0/2, the 1/1, the 1/2 and the 2/2, and arrange them in exactly the same shape, but this time do it so that each of the four sides of the square contains the same number of pips.

Triangular Terror**

For this puzzle you require the same 6 dominoes as above. Arrange them to form an equilateral triangle like the one below.

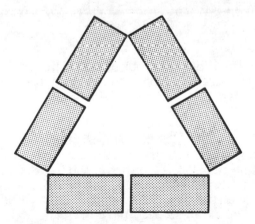

The problem is that you must make sure that each of the three sides of the triangle contains exactly the same number of pips, but at the same time you must make sure that none of the joins match.

First Rectangle**

Since we've had a couple of square problems and a triangular one, it's about time we had a rectangular one. For this you'll need the same 6 dominoes, the 0/0, the 0/1, the 0/2, the 1/1, the 1/2, the 2/2, and the same quick wittedness as before. You have got to use the dominoes to create a rectangle that looks exactly like this:

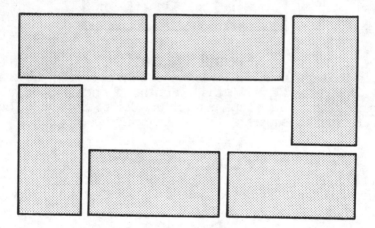

The puzzling part of the problem comes in making sure that each of the four sides of the rectangle contains precisely the same number of pips.

The Three Rectangles**

Take the fifteen lowest dominoes in the set (the 0/0, the 0/1, the 0/2, the 0/3, the 0/4, the 1/1, the 1/2, the 1/3, the 1/4, the 2/2, the 2/3, the 2/4, the 3/3, the 3/4, the 4/4) and form 3 separate rectangles with them, so that all the joins are matching. Each of the rectangles should look like the one at the top of page 133.

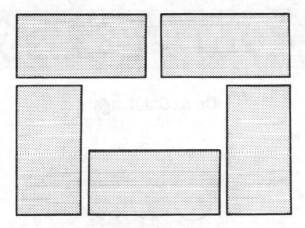

Giant Square***

Take the 10 lowest dominoes in the set (the 0/0, the 0/1, the 0/2, the 0/3, the 1/1, the 1/2, the 1/3, the 2/2, the 2/3 and the 3/3) but you must make sure that the number of pips on each of the 4 sides of the Giant Square is the same and that none of the joins match. Here's the shape you should create for this puzzle.

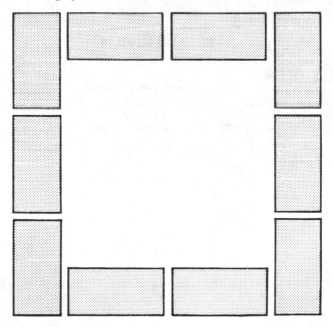

Cross Challenge*

Take six coins and arrange them on the table in the shape of a cross, like this:

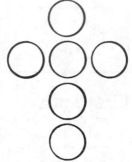

Now move just one of the coins and create two rows with four coins in each row.

Square Challenge*

Take 12 coins and arrange them on the table in the shape of a square, like this:

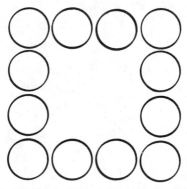

As you can see, there are four coins along each side of the square. Using the same 12 coins, form another square, but with the new square, see to it that you can count five coins along each side.

Circular Challenge**

Take 6 coins and lay them out on the table in two columns like this:

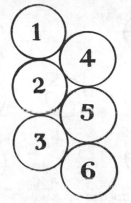

Now all you've got to do is make a circle of coins in just three moves! You can only move one coin at a time and once you've moved it to its new position it must be touching at least two other coins.

Pyramid Challenge**

Take 10 coins and lay them out on the table in the shape of a pyramid, like this:

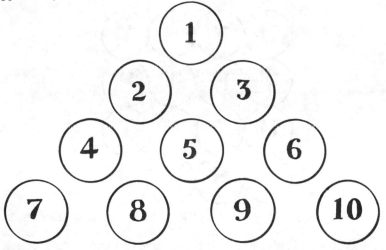

Now move just three of the coins and turn the pyramid upside down.

The H Problem**

Take seven coins and arrange them in a pattern to look like the letter H.

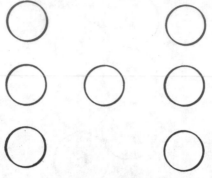

As you can see, counting the diagonal lines as well as the vertical and horizontal, you have five rows with three coins in each row. Now add an extra two coins to the pattern and create a new pattern that incorporates ten rows with three coins in each row.

Sixteen Coins**

Take sixteen coins and arrange them on the table in four columns, with heads and tails alternating, like this:

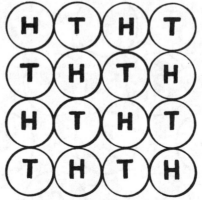

Now all you've got to do is rearrange the coins so that the coins in each of the four vertical columns are alike. That's to say you've got to end up with one column of heads, one column of tails, one of heads, one of tails. The only problem is: your hand is only allowed to touch *two* of the sixteen coins!

Six in a Row**

Find three 5p pieces and three 10p pieces and lay them out in a neat row, like this:

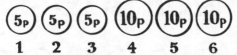

Now, in just three moves, moving two adjacent coins at a time, you have got to make a row of coins where the 10p and the 5p pieces *alternate*. There must be no gaps between the coins.

Eight in a Row**

Find four 5p pieces and four 10p pieces and lay them out in a row, like this:

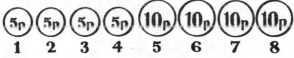

Now, in four moves, moving two adjacent coins at a time, you have got to make a row in which there are no gaps and the 10p and 5p pieces alternate.

Head Over Heels***

Take eight coins and lay them out in a circle, all heads up and looking like this:

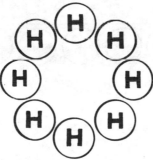

Starting from any coin you like, and moving clockwise, or anti-clockwise, count one, two, three, four, and turn over the fourth coin so that it's tails up. Starting again from any coin that's heads up, repeat the process. Keep at it until all the coins but one are tails up.

Nine-a-side**

Take thirty-two coins and lay them out in a square so that there are nine coins on each side of the square.

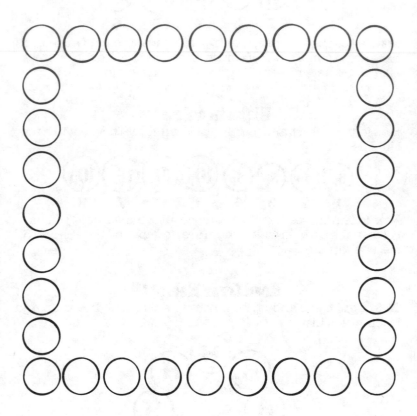

Now remove four coins and rearrange the remaining twenty-eight so that there are still nine coins on each side of the square.

Now remove a further four coins and rearrange the remaining twenty-four so that there are still nine coins on each side of the square!

Finally, remove four more coins and rearrange the twenty that are left so that you can still count nine coins on each side of the square!

Odd Lines*

Take twelve coins and lay them out in a very familiar pattern, so that you end up with three straight lines and an odd number of coins in each line.

Seven Rows*

Take twelve coins and lay them out in seven rows, with four coins in each row.

Nine Rows**

Take nineteen coins and lay them out in nine rows, with five coins in each row.

Twelve Rows***

Take twenty-one coins and lay them out in twelve rows with five coins in each row.

Fifteen Rows***

Take sixteen coins and lay them out in fifteen rows, with four coins in each row.

WHY ARE CONUNDRUMS THAT CANNOT BE SOLVED LIKE A MAN DISAPPOINTED BY HIS VISITORS?

BECAUSE THERE IS A HOST PUT OUT AND NOT ONE GUESSED.

TANGRAMS

A tangram is a geometric dissection puzzle, devised in ancient China, in which seven standard pieces (two small triangles, one medium size triangle, two large triangles, one square and one rhomboid) are used to make images of various objects. To attempt these puzzles you will need a set of tangrams, which can be cut from a single square like this:

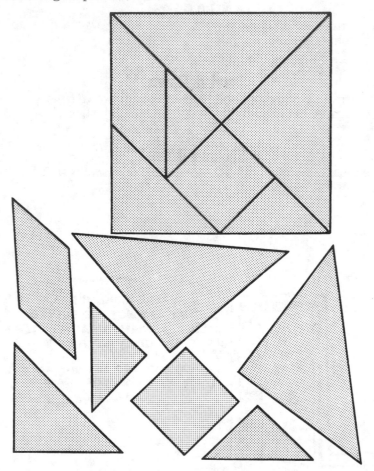

Shapely Tangrams*

Use all your tangrams to create each of these shapes.

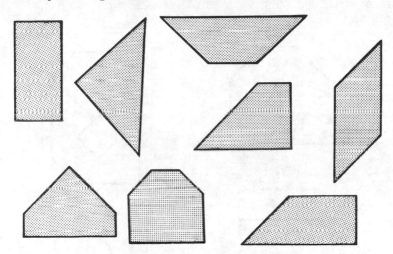

Number Tangrams**

With your tangrams try to construct, one at a time, the numbers one, two, three, four, five, six, seven, and eight, as shown.

Alphabetical Tangrams***

Attempt to construct the entire alphabet with your tangrams, one letter at a time. You must use all seven pieces and none of them must overlap.

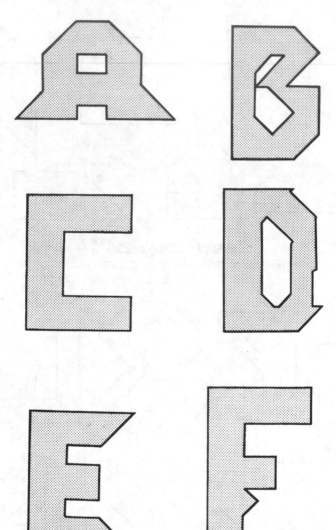

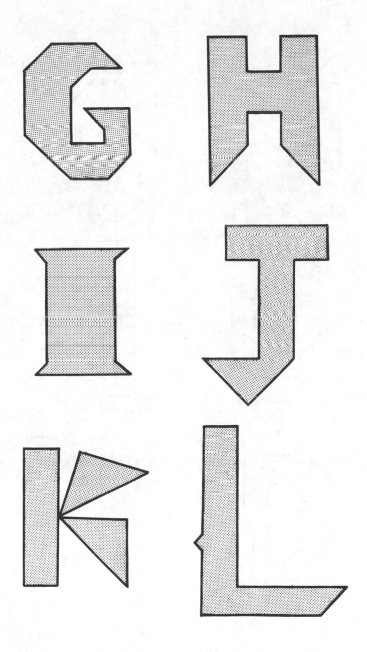

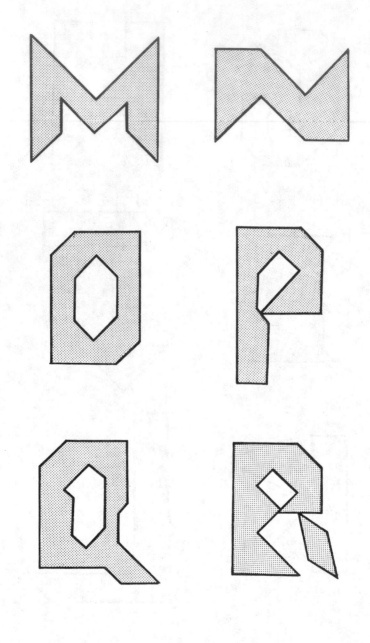

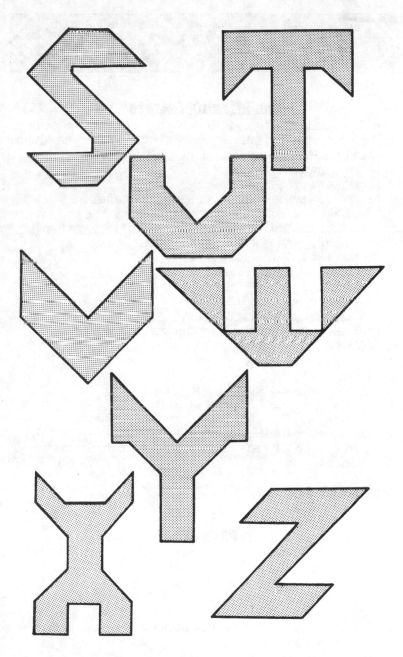

The Missing Letters*

Here is a puzzle that's easy to work out if you do it with pencil and paper, but pretty perplexing if you try it without – so try it without.

Think of all the letters of the alphabet.

Now take away the second.

Now take away the twenty-second.

Now take away the one that comes before the last one you took away.

Now take away the letter O and the letter that comes after O.

Now take away the sixth, fifth and fourth letters.

Now take away X and Y.

Now take away the third letter.

Now add Q.

Now take away T.

Now take away the seventh letter.

Now take away H and the letter that comes seven places before it.

Now take away the letter that comes before R.

Now take away R.

Now take away the remaining vowel.

Now take away the three letters that follow it.

Now take away N and the letter that comes before it.

Now take away the last letter of the alphabet.

Now take away all the remaining consonants in the word 'stew'.

What are you left with?

What's What*

Here are twenty questions to make you think. They aren't as simple as they sound.

1. What is it that no one wishes to have, but no one wishes to lose?
2. What is it that everyone believes is always coming, but never really arrives?

3. What is it that you can't hold for half an hour, even though it's lighter than feather?
4. What is it that's put on the table, cut and passed, but never eaten?
5. What is it that occurs four times in every week, twice in every month, but only once in a year?
6. What is full of holes, but still holds water?
7. What is the one thing you break when you name it?
8. What is always in front of you, even though you can never see it?
9. What is lengthened by being cut at both ends?
10. What always weighs the same, whatever its size?
11. What is large enough to hold a pig and yet small enough to hold in your hand?
12. What is it that the person who makes it doesn't need, the person who buys it doesn't use for himself and the person who uses it does so without knowing it?
13. What is it that everyone, no matter how careful they happen to be, always overlooks?
14. What can be right, but never wrong?
15. What lives on its own substance, but dies the moment it has devoured itself?
16. What is it that has no length, no breadth, no thickness, but when it is given to you you definitely feel?
17. What is bought by the yard, but worn out by the foot?
18. What will always be down however high up it is?
19. What goes from New York to Philadelphia without moving?
20. With what could you fill a barrel to make it lighter than when it is empty?

My Three Sons*

I have a Russian friend who has three sons. The first son was called Rab and became a lawyer. The second son was called Ymra and became a soldier. The third son became a sailor.

What was he called?
Why?

Oddition*

Write down five odd numbers so that when you add them up they total 14.

Musical Meanings*

Here are some well-known musical terms. All you've got to do is
work out their meanings.

1. Does **presto** mean:
   a) fast?
   b) slow?
   c) quietly?
   d) loudly?

2. Does **adagio** mean:
   a) very lightly?
   b) very quickly?
   c) very bouncily?
   d) very slowly?

3. Does **largo** mean:
   a) in the style of a lively dance?
   b) in the style of a funeral march?
   c) in a fast, raucous style?
   d) in a slow, dignified style?

4. Does **fortissimo** mean:
   a) very fast?
   b) very slow?
   c) very loud?
   d) very soft?

5. Does **dolce** mean:
   a) angrily?
   b) sorrowfully?
   c) sweetly?
   d) tearfully?

6. Does **crescendo** mean:
   a) singing very loudly?
   b) decreasing the volume
      slowly?
   c) singing very softly?
   d) increasing the volume
      slowly?

Weak Word**

Can you think of a fifteen-letter word in which the only vowel is the
letter E which is used three times in the word?

Unpunctuated*

All punctuation has been omitted in the strange sentences that
follow. Can you supply the correct punctuation and make sense of
them? To make it more complicated, they are not necessarily
single sentences.

1. he said that that that that woman said ought to have been
   which

2. it was and I said not but

3. the murderer spoke angrily half an hour after he was hanged

4. time flies you cannot they pass by at such irregular intervals

5. Esau Wood saw a saw saw wood as no other wood saw Wood saw would saw wood of all the wood saws Wood ever saw saw wood Wood never saw a wood saw that would saw wood as the wood saw Wood saw saw wood would saw wood and I never saw a wood saw that would saw wood as the wood saw Wood saw would saw until I saw Wood saw wood with the wood saw Esau Wood saw saw wood.

When you've punctuated number five try saying it to yourself ten times without making any mistakes!

Composers' Corner*

Here, listed in the order of their birth, are the names of some of the world's greatest and most famous composers. In amongst the real names, dates and nationalities, are five phoneys. Can you spot them?

George Friedrich Handel (1685-1759) German
Johann Sebastian Bach (1685-1750) German
Franz Joseph Haydn (1732-1809) Austrian
Rudolph Von Smettow (1740-1801) German
Wolfgang Amadeus Mozart (1756-1791) Austrian
Hector Adolph Buzzi (1769-1812) Swiss
Ludwig Van Beethoven (1770-1827) German
Gioacchino Rossini (1792-1868) Italian
Franz Peter Schubert (1797-1828) Austrian
Mikhail Ivanovitch Glinka (1804-1857) Russian
Frederic Chopin (1810-1849) Polish
Franz Liszt (1811-1886) Hungarian
Richard Wagner (1813-1883) German
Giuseppe Pizzo (1813-1901) Italian
Johannes Brahms (1833-1897) German
Georges Bizet (1838-1875) French
Peter Ilyich Tchaikovsky (1840-1893) Russian
Arthur Sullivan (1842-1900) English
Igor Plinplonski (1850-1937) Russian
Gustav Mahler (1860-1911) Austrian
Richard Strauss (1864-1949) German
Kurt Barsolova (1864-1956) Hungarian
Jean Sibelius (1865-1957) Finnish

The Nelson Touch**

Admiral Lord Nelson is standing on top of his column in the middle of Trafalgar Square facing due West.

Given the instructions:
RIGHT TURN! ABOUT TURN! LEFT TURN!

which way would he end up facing?

What and Where?*

Some of the world's most famous landmarks have got into a muddle here. Can you unjumble them and decide where you would have to go to find them.

1. The Leaning Tower of Bridge.
2. The Taj Falls.
3. Buckingham Needle.
4. The Niagara Grande.
5. The Eiffel Mahal.
6. The Great Building.
7. The Rio Tower.
8. The Golden Gate Pisa.
9. Cleopatra's Wall.
10. The Empire State Palace.

Dotty Problems**

Without lifting your pencil from the page and without going over the same dot twice, join these twenty-five dots with eight straight lines.

If you don't know what a rebus is, don't worry. U R never 2 old or YY 2 learn something new. My dictionary definition of a rebus is 'an enigmatic representation of a name or a word or a phrase by pictures or letters or numbers or other words or phrases.'

So if 'ime' is the rebus way of saying: 'Not before time', (i.e. No "T" before time). And this:

B
E

– is B on E or BONE!

Top Ten**

1. What's this?

ONE ANOTHER
ONE ANOTHER
ONE ANOTHER
ONE ANOTHER
ONE ANOTHER
ONE ANOTHER

2. Popeye would have loved this. What is it?

AC SP H

3. What is the name of this young lady?

MARY
2,000 pounds

4. This is a rebus fit for a court of law. What does it mean?

STAND   OATH
U   UR

5. Have you been to this play?

ADO

ADO   ADO

ADO   O   ADO

ADO   ADO

ADO

6. There are six letters here, all pointing to a cold climate. What are they?

WETHER

7. What word is this?

$\boxed{U}\ \begin{matrix} C \\ T \end{matrix}$

8. What does this mean?

STAND	TAKE	TO	TAKING
I	YOU	THROW	MY

9. Here is a well-known phrase. Can you spot it?

ONALLE

10. This is the alcoholic's lament to his bottle. Can you translate it into sober English?

OICURMT

Finally*

Rearrange these six letters and what do you find?

D E E H N T

SOLUTIONS

Mr. Thyme's Puzzle
'A nod's as good as a wink to a blind horse.'

Verbal Display
1. **To hustle** is to push and hurry.
2. **To brawl** is to fight.
3. **To gratify** is to please.
4. **To munch** is to eat.
5. **To repulse** is to drive off an attack.
6. **To submerge** is to go under water.
7. **To distort** is to put something out of shape.
8. **To meditate** is to think deeply.
9. **To wallop** is to hit someone or something.
10. **To somnambulate** is to walk in one's sleep.

Collecting Collectives
1. A shrewdness of apes
2. A cete of badgers
3. A shoal of bass
4. A sloth of bears
5. An army of caterpillars
6. A clowder of cats
7. A drove of cattle
8. A peep of chickens
9. A murder of crows
10. A dule of doves
11. A school of fish
12. A skulk of foxes
13. A gaggle of geese
14. A husk of hares
15. A cast of hawks
16. A brood of hens
17. A siege of herons
18. A haras of horses
19. A smack of jellyfish
20. A kindle of kittens
21. A deceit of lapwings
22. A leap of leopards
23. A pride of lions
24. A plague of locusts
25. A watch of nightingales
26. A parliament of owls

Homophones

1. a. Right b. Rite
2. a. Band b. Banned
3. a. Maize b. Maze
4. a. Ascent b. Assent
5. a. Foul b. Fowl
6. a. Pact b. Packed
7. a. Bowl b. Bowl
8. a. Ball b. Bawl
9. a. Seine b. Sane
10. a. Place b. Plaice

ANAGRAMS

Head Over Heels
Somersault

European Cities
1. VENICE   2. NAPLES

3. ATHENS
4. REIMS
5. SIENA
6. BASLE
7. PARIS
8. CORK
9. OSLO
10. ROME
11. LENINGRAD
12. TOLEDO
13. OSTEND
14. GENEVA

World Cities

1. MINSK
2. TULSA
3. TUNIS
4. LAGOS
5. KABUL
6. SEOUL
7. SIMLA
8. LIMA
9. RENO
10. LAS VEGAS
11. SAN DIEGO
12. DETROIT
13. TIJUANA
14. TANGIER
15. TUCSON
16. TEHRAN
17. MADRAS
18. DARWIN
19. MANILA
20. DENVER
21. VALENCE
22. VILNA
23. KYOTO
24. ACRE

Occupy Yourself

1. GAOLER
2. WELDER
3. WARDER
4. HATTER
5. AIRMAN
6. EDITOR
7. PRIEST
8. SINGER
9. TAILOR
10. DANCER
11. TRADER
12. ARTIST
13. DOCKER
14. PARSON
15. WARDEN
16. TUTOR
17. MASON
18. NURSE
19. DIVER
20. BAKER
21. DYER
22. ACTRESS
23. TEACHER
24. RAILMAN
25. DENTIST

Gladstone

We want a mild legislator; Will mislead a great town; Wit so great will lead man; A man to wield great wills.

You Name It

1. MEG
2. DORA
3. NEIL
4. MILES
5. ROSIE
6. RHODA
7. LAURA
8. GRETA
9. ETHEL
10. EDGAR
11. MABEL
12. MOIRA
13. DELIA
14. CILLA
15. TESSA
16. STELLA
17. RODNEY
18. GLENDA
19. GLYNIS
20. MARTIN
21. STEVEN
22. INGRID
23. THELMA
24. TERESA

Problematic Phrases

1. PARISHIONERS
2. FUNERAL
3. INFECTION
4. MISFORTUNE
5. STEAMINESS
6. ENDEARMENTS
7. HUSTLERS
8. WAITRESS
9. REMUNERATION
10. PUNISHMENT
11. VIOLENCE
12. FILLED
13. LEGISLATION
14. MILITARISM
15. FAMILIES
16. UPHOLSTERERS
17. DESPERATION
18. CATALOGUES

Presidential Poser

Ronald Reagan

One Over the Eight

A STITCH IN TIME SAVES NINE

Prime Poser

Margaret Thatcher

HIDDEN WORDS

Alpha Plus

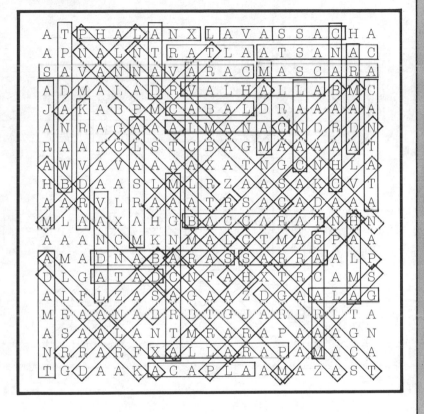

X-Tract

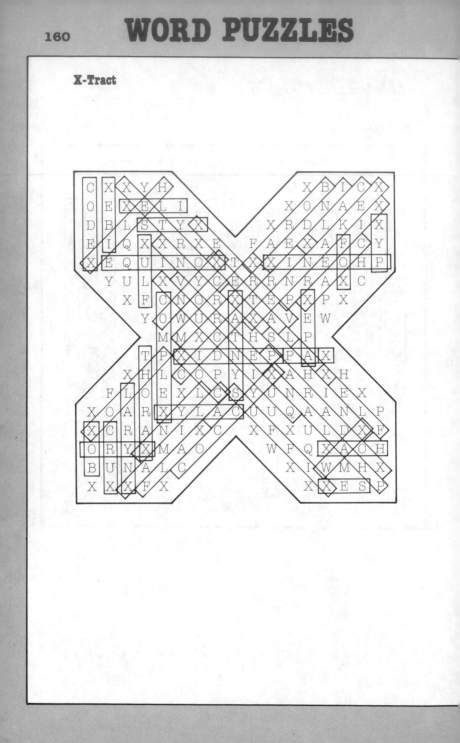

Quoting the Bard

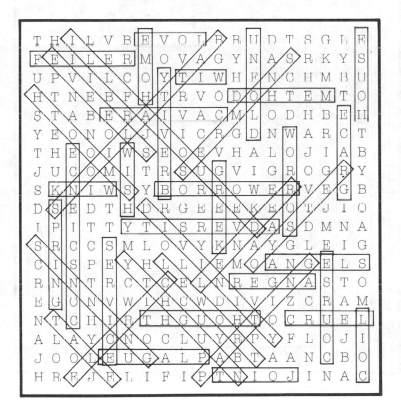

Parlez-vous?

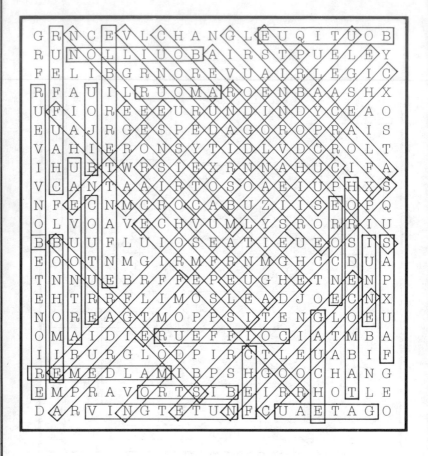

The Haystack

```
E L D E N E E D E L N E E N E D L
L E E N E D L E N E E D E L N E E
D E E L E N D L E E D E N E E D L
E D N E L E E N E L E E L E E N E
N E E L D E E D N L E D E N D E N
E N L E E D E L E D E E N E L E L
E E D E N N E E L E D L E N D E E
D E D E L E E D N E E L D E L L D
N L E N E L D L E N E E L D N E E
E D E D L N E E E D L E N E E D L
L E L D E L N E L E N E D E D N E
N E E D N E D E D E E D E N E L L
N E L D E E E E L N E E L E D E E
N E D E L D E N E E D L N E E L D
E N D E E L E N E N E E L D E E E
E L E N N E E E D L E N E E L N N
E E D L E N E L E N E L E N E N D
```

Two of a Kind

1. JESUS CHRIST
2. SANTA CLAUS

The letters are exchanged for the ones that follow them in the alphabet. Hence, J becomes K, E becomes F, S becomes T, and so on.

Film Fun

1. THE SOUND OF MUSIC
2. ONE FLEW OVER THE CUCKOO'S NEST
3. THE FRENCH LIEUTENANT'S WOMAN
4. STAR WARS
5. SATURDAY NIGHT FEVER
6. EVIL UNDER THE SUN
7. CHARIOTS OF FIRE
8. SUPERMAN
9. ANIMAL HOUSE
10. FOR YOUR EYES ONLY

Word Numbers

1. RECTIFY
2. PATRIARCH
3. HERALD
4. GROTESQUE
5. VENTILATE
6. TREMULOUS
7. SNIGGER
8. REUNION
9. PROTEIN
10. MONSTROUS
11. LUMINARY
12. IDIOSYNCRASY
13. FRUSTRATE
14. DRAUGHTSMAN
15. DISTANCE

Novel Quiz

1. BLEAK HOUSE (Charles Dickens) 2. NINETEEN EIGHTY FOUR (George Orwell) 3. EMMA (Jane Austen) 4. JANE EYRE (Charlotte Brontë) 5. WINNIE THE POOH (A.A. Milne)
6. PERSUASION (Jane Austen)
7. THE TALE OF PETER RABBIT (Beatrix Potter) 8. FROM RUSSIA WITH LOVE (Ian Fleming)
9. FRANKENSTEIN (Mary Shelley) 10. LITTLE WOMEN (Louisa May Alcott)

Sounds Familiar

Have you any eggs? Yes we have eggs. Have you any ham? Yes we have ham. OK I'll have ham and eggs.

Mixed Faith

1. Well done thou good and faithful servant.
2. His banner over me was love.
3. I am that I am.
4. I am escaped with the skin of my teeth.
5. I came not to send peace, but a sword.
6. He that hath ears to hear let him hear.
7. He came unto his own and his own received him not.
8. Who against hope believed in hope.
9. What I have written I have written.
10. Let your yea be yea, and your nay, nay.
11. A man after his own heart.

False Start

ALL THE FIRST AND ALL THE LAST LETTERS ARE FALSE.

Vowel Play

PERSEVERE YE PERFECT MEN EVER KEEP THESE PRECEPTS TEN

Unnatural Break

ALL OUR LIVES WE ARE CRUSHED BY THE WEIGHT OF WORDS.

Alphabetical Extractions

1. Evergreen	2. Rhythm
3. Minimum	4. Quinquireme
5. Anagram	6. Nineteen
7. Gargling	8. Wigwam
9. Cyclic	10. Puppies
11. Kinky	12. Gypsy
13. Success	14. Xerxes
15. Thirty	16. Fanfare
17. Evasive	18. Suburb
19. Horror	20. Liable
21. Jazzy	22. Damned
23. Ululate	24. Jejune
25. Voodoo	26. Ironic

WORD PUZZLES

The Word

Excommunication.

E 10 100 0 1000 1000 UNI 100 AT X N

E X C O M M UNI C AT 10 N

Full Marx

You need the missing vowels, because with them you will have the titles of six of the Marx Brothers films: Animal Crackers, Monkey Business, Horse Feathers, Duck Soup, A Night at the Opera and A Day at the Races.

WORD CIRCLES AND LADDERS AND SQUARES

Word Circles

1. COERCION
2. SCIATICA
3. CYCLAMEN
4. BELIEVER
5. SYNDROME
6. EDUCATOR
7. ORIGINAL
8. HYSTERIC
9. HARMONIC
10. GARGOYLE
11. MYSTICAL
12. HACIENDA
13. MNEMONIC
14. METAPHOR
15. GLYCERIN
16. EULOGIST

Magic Spell

There are 1,024 ways to spell out **ABRACADABRA**

Six-Letter Odd-Ends

1. PAGODA
2. ASTHMA
3. CHERUB
4. ORCHID
5. PERIOD
6. ABSURD
7. ANNEXE
8. BEHALF
9. ENGULF
10. BORZOI
11. CUDGEL
12. FULFIL
13. CONSUL
14. RHYTHM
15. VICTIM
16. FATHOM

17. FLAXEN
18. SOLEMN
19. GAZEBO
20. STUCCO
21. ROCOCO
22. STEREO
23. STUDIO
24. DYNAMO
25. CUCKOO
26. EMBRYO
27. BAZAAR
28. JAGUAR
29. METEOR
30. LIQUOR
31. ZEPHYR
32. CANVAS
33. HAGGIS
34. NOUGAT
35. LARIAT
36. CRAVAT
37. LANDAU
38. ORMOLU
39. CONVEX
40. GALAXY
41. CHINTZ
42. QUARTZ

Bird Fivers

Crane

In for a Spell

All, alm, bail, bilk, fed, fog, fop, for, form, gory, hilt, him, ilk, jab, jail, jilt, kilt, limn, milk, nog, prong, pronged, pyx, slim, slut.

Musical Spell

Fife, flute, lute, tuba, oboe, trumpet, tambourine, pipe, viol, viola, violin, drum, piano, gong, tabour, tabret.

Fill-ins

1. RAT	2. SAPS	3. CARES
ART	ASPS	SCARE
TAR	PASS	RACES
	SPAS	

4. RIPEST	5. TEAMS	6. POST
PRIEST	STEAM	POTS
SPRITE	MEATS	TOPS
	MATES	STOP
	TAMES	SPOT

7. POOL	8. MEAD
POLO	DAME
LOOP	MADE

WORD PUZZLES

Word Ladders

1. PIG
wig
wag
way
say
STY

2. FOUR
foul
fool
foot
fort
fore
fire
FIVE

3. WHEAT
cheat
cheap
cheep
creep
creed
breed
BREAD

4. NOSE
note
cote
core
corn
coin
CHIN

5. TEARS
sears
stars
stare
stale
stile
SMILE

6. HARE
hark
hack
sack
sock
soak
soap
SOUP

7. PITCH
pinch
winch
wench
tench
tenth
TENTS

8. EYE
dye
die
did
LID

9. PITY
pits
pins
fins
find
fond
food
GOOD

10. POOR
boor
book
rook
rock
rick
RICH

11. TREE
free
flee
fled
feed
weed
weld
wold
WOOD

12. GRASS
crass
cress
tress
trees
frees
freed
greed
GREEN

13. FLOUR
floor
flood
blood
brood
broad
BREAD

14. TEA
sea
set
sot
HOT

15. MINE
mint
mist
most
moat
coat
COAL

16. BLACK
blank
blink
clink
chink
chine
whine
WHITE

17. WITCH
winch
wench
tench
tenth
tents
tints
tilts
tills
fills
falls
fails
fairs
FAIRY

18. WINTER
winner
winder
wander
warder
harder
harper
hamper
damper
damped
dammed
dimmed
dimmer
simmer
SUMMER

Ici Français

1. See you soon.
2. Farewell.
3. Affair of the heart.
4. Trusted assistant.
5. In fashion.
6. Familiar with.
7. Ahead of one's time.
8. Exquisite miniature.
9. Love letter.
10. Tired of pleasure.
11. Decorative scroll or frame.
12. Everyone to his own taste.
13. Final blow.
14. Low cut of a dress.
15. Seemingly to have experienced before.
16. The right word.
17. Pseudonym.
18. Out of the ordinary.
19. Out of date.
20. Daring.

Hidden Countries

1. Iran, Vietnam
2. Malta, India
3. Sweden, Lebanon
4. Panama, Spain
5. Tonga, Togo
6. Lesotho, Ghana
7. Dahomey, Nepal
8. Peru, Uganda
9. Chad, Andorra
10. Gabon, Mali

Origins

1. French 2. French 3. Latin
4. Spanish 5. French
6. Italian 7. Latin 8. Arabic
9. Yiddish 10. Portuguese
11. Haitian 12. Polynesian
13. Swedish 14. Japanese
15. Hindi 16. Turkish
17. Hindi 18. Norwegian
19. Hindi 20. Greek
21. Latin 22. Greek
23. Greek 24. Spanish

Slang words

Whistle and flute (Suit),
Trouble and strife (Wife),
Rosie Lee (Tea),
Pig's ear (Beer),
Dolly varden (Garden),
Daisy roots (Boots),
China plate (Mate),
Butcher's hook (Look),
Bees and honey (Money),
Apples and pears (Stairs).

English Spoken Here

1. à la carte
2. à propos
3. bagatelle
4. bon appetit
5. bon mot
6. bric à brac
7. carte blanche
8. c'est la vie
9. clique
10. compère
11. coquette
12. crème de la crème
13. debût 14. faux pas
15. genre 16. mélange
17. piquant
18. tour de force
19. vis à vis 20. beau geste

Down Under

Aussie	Australia/Australian
Bathers	Swimming costume
Billabong	Pond
Bowser	Petrol pump
Bush (the)	Countryside
Cobber	Mate
Didgeridoo	Trumpet
Dingo	Australian wild dog
Dinkum	Honest
Duds	Best clothes
Goanna	Lizard
Good on you	Well done!
Grazier	Farmer
Gum tree	Eucalyptus tree
Jackeroo	Pupil on sheep/cattle station
Joey	Baby kangaroo
Jumbuck	Sheep
Lollies	Sweets
Milk bar	Dairy & general grocery shop
Moke	Horse
Noah's ark	Shark
Nong	Idiot
Paddy melon	Small wallaby
Pommy	Englishman/woman
Port	Suitcase
Postie	Postman
Sheila	Girl/woman
Swag	Bundle of belongings

SECTION 1

Spot the Difference
1. Shop

Spot the Difference
2. Fun in the Sun

Spot the Mistake
1. Bonjour

Spot the Mistake
2. Cor Blimey!

Apart from the apples instead of onions, both drivers are on the wrong side of the road and Marseille should be 650 kilometres from Paris.

It is 1953 but "Mary Poppins" was not on show until 1964, the Post Office Tower was built in 1965 and there was no Prince of Wales then.

SECTION 2

Spot the Difference
3. Departure Time

Spot the Mistake
3. Ex Libris

"Wind in the Willows" is by
Kenneth Grahame, "Lord of the
Flies" should be listed under
Fiction and "Born Free" should be
under Wild Life.

SHADOW SHOWS

1. A fox

2. A bulldog

3. A human
face

4. A rustic
farmer

5. An
elephant

6. A rabbit

7. A bird
in flight

8. A dog,
tongue out

9. A parrot

10. A red
Indian

SECTION 3

**Spot the Difference
4. School's Out**

**Spot the Difference
5. Waiter**

**Spot the Mistake
4. Victorian Parlour**

**Spot the Mistake
5. Pharoah's Folly**

It's 1864, but Kipling was not born until 1865, there were no telephones until 1876, the song was not yet written and The Times only had classified ads on the front.

Hinges, power points and padlocks are all out of place in Pharoah's tomb, as are prehistoric cave paintings and Greek inscriptions!

NUMBER FUN

Twenty Questions

1. c	2. d
3. c	4. a
5. c	6. b
7. b and d	8. b
9. d	10. c
11. a	12. d
13. d	14. b
15. b	16. b
17. c	18. d
19. b	20. c

What Next?

a. 6   b. N (for Ninety)

c. 15

d. 5 (the numbers give the years of the two World Wars)

e. 35   f. T (for Ten)

g. 27

h. Any number at all: the numbers were picked at random and so there is no sequence!

Pick a Number

1. 1,000,000,000
2. 4,195 miles
3. 90,000,000
4. 40
5. 291,000,000
6. 1.6093
7. 4,700,000,000 years
8. 10,000m^3
9. 1,000,000,000,000,000,000
10. 56m

Punch and Judy

Punch is 52. Judy is 39.

Monday to Friday

49

AD/BC

99 years old. There was no year 0.

Next Please

1. 31: the numbers are those of the days in the month, starting with January.

2. 48: the number doubles each time.

3. 1: the numbers are 1837 to 1901. The reign of Queen Victoria.

4. 65: each time you double the previous number and then subtract 1.

5. 9: each time two numbers are followed by a third which is the figure you get when the two numbers are multiplied together.

6. 1: the figures represent the number of times a clock will strike if it strikes once every half-hour as well as striking on the hour; the series here begins at 11.30.

7. 9: 1 (+5 =) 6, 2 (+5 =) 7. 3 (+5 =) 8. 4 (+5 =) 9.

8. 536: you must subtract 101 each time.

9. 8589934592: each number is multiplied by half of itself to form the next number.

10. 250: it's simply 1000 divided first by 9, then by 8, then by 7, then by 6, then by 5, then by 4.

Big Shot

Johnny who saw the smoke knew of it first; Bobby who heard the shot, second; and Willie who saw the bullet hit the water, third. Light travels faster than sound and sound faster than a bullet.

Now What?
20. The figures represent the coins and notes in the British currency from ½p to £20.

How Much?
£100

Where There's a Will
The widow would receive £205.13.

Not so Silly Willie
£10,737,418.24

Drink Up
£1 each. There was a grandfather, father and son.

The Lost Note
The cost of the room was £27 minus the £2, therefore £25. The error comes from mistakenly adding £27 and £2 and getting the misleading figure of £29.

Share Out
Alex will receive 2,500 pennies, Bobby 1,500 and Colin 700 pennies.

Bow and Arrow
The bow cost £20.50 and the arrow 50p.

The Pools Winner
£19,005

Auntie Nellie
£160

See a Man About a Dog
£49

A Pound of Apples
The two ways of selling are only identical when the number of apples sold at 30 for £1 and 20 for £1 is in the proportion of 30 to 20.

Inflation
£25.25; £28.25; £30.25; £36.25

Your Number's Up
The prices quoted were for house numbers at 12 pence per digit. A number 6 digit cost him 12 pence.

Mugger's Money
From Mr Ascot £88. From Mr Berkshire £44.

Long Time
The faster watch gains on the slower one at the rate of three minutes every hour. After 20 hours, the faster one will be ahead by exactly one hour.

On Strike
300 times

Long Hands
55/143 minutes past 12 or 60/143 past 1.

Felines and Rodents
6 cats can devour 100 rats in 100 minutes (6,000 seconds)

Stitches in Time
18

Timetable
It was 5 and 5/11 minutes past 1 o'clock.

Party Time
It began at 59 minutes past ten. It is now 54 minutes past eleven.

Digital Clock
0. The figures represent the sequence on a digital clock showing hour, minutes, seconds, as one p.m. approaches.

Quarter of a Century

9	11	18	5	22
3	25	7	14	16
12	19	1	23	10
21	8	15	17	4
20	2	24	6	13

Radioactive Problem
You need only move 3 containers. Replace 6 by 3, and 9 by 6, and put 9 where 3 was:

13	3	14
11	10	9
6	17	7

Nine-a-side
This is how the butler did it:

3	3	3		4	1	4
3		3		1		1
3	3	3		4	1	4

Misplacement
The 7 and the 12 must be interchanged.

Amazing!
The totals of rows, columns, and diagonals is 19,998. The four corners also total 19,998. The amazing property is that if you turn the square upside down, it still works, each row, column and diagonal will total 19,998.

Mini Quiz
1. $1815 \times 20 = 36300$
2. $36300 \times 31 = 1125300$
3. $1125300 \div 10 = 112530$
4. $112530 + 10,000,000 = 10112530$
5. $10112530 - 1805 = 10110725$
6. $10110725 \div 80 = 126384 \cdot 06$

Talking Calculators
1. 379919
2. 7105
3. 4509
4. 3704
5. 57738
6. 378809
7. 57108
8. 5355378

The Percent Puzzle

$0 + 920 - 156 \cdot 25 + 129 \cdot 78 +$
$3518 \cdot 17 - 4414 \cdot 08 + 666 \cdot 66 + 1600$
$-650 - 850 + 42 \cdot 68 + 450 \cdot 24 -$
$163 \cdot 55 + 409 \cdot 26 + 701 \cdot 15 + 372 \cdot 36$
$+ 3055 \cdot 25 - 3750 + 4907 \cdot 25 +$
$1469 \cdot 75 - 6561 - 1697 \cdot 67 = 0$

To the Letter

1. 155,3125	2. 375
3. 787.5	4. 14,914285
5. 4.2777778	6. 2,111112
7. 0.52	8. 20
9. 123.09375	10. 107

Dictionary Digits

1. SOS	2. LOLLIPOP
3. BOGGLE	4. HI
5. HOHOHO	6. ODOE
7. HOG	8. EEL

Common Factor

1. 3784	2. 3159
3. 1395	4. 1827
5. 2187	6. 1435

In all sums the digits in the answer are the same as those in the multiplier.

Multiplication Digits

1. 1963
  x 4
—
7852
	2. 198
	  x 27
	—
	5346

3. 1738
  x 4
—
6952
	4. 159
	  x 48
	—
	7632

DIGITAL DILEMMAS

The Weigh In

One grapefruit weighs 600 gms

Add and Subtract

(a) $5 - 4 + 3 + 2 - 1 = 5$
(b) $2 + 2 - 3 + 4 - 5 = 0$
(c) $5 + 3 - 1 + 3 - 5 = 5$
(d) $12 + 3 - 4 + 5 - 6 = 10$

999999?

$99^{99}/_{99}$

Drunkards

$140 \div 3 = 46\frac{2}{3}$ days

Keep the Doctor Away

Benet ate 6 apples.

Tea Time

4 ounces

Bookworm

The important part of this problem is to remember how we stand books on a shelf.

The first page of volume 1 is indicated by the left arrow, and the last page of volume 6 by the right arrow. Beginning and ending at these points the worm passes through 10 covers totalling 30 millimeters, and 4 texts totalling 12 centimeters, for a complete journey of 15 centimetres.

Stick in the Mud

36 feet. One ninth (or

two-eighteenths) of the log was in
the mud: 4 feet. Five-sixths (or
fifteen-eighteenths) was above
water: 30 feet. And 2 feet was in the
water, making 36 feet in all.

Fishy Problem
45 pounds

Number Scrabble
17531908 + 7088062 = 24619970

Baby Monkeys
3 lbs

Farm Fare
3

Talking Turkey
20 kg

What's the Difference?
12 km^3

Two Dozen
22 + 2 = 24

Four Fives
$5^5/_5.5 = 6½$

Sum Subtraction
$$\begin{array}{r} 555555555 = 45 \\ \text{x} \quad 99999 = 45 \\ \hline 5554555556 = 45 \end{array}$$

Ten Not Out
T E N

Father and Son
80

Fowl-up
28 eggs

CONUNDRUMS

Value the Difference
Six dozen dozen = 864

Half a dozen dozen = 72

So the difference between them is
864 − 72 = 792

Family Problems
There are four boys and three girls.

Poor but Honest
1. So no one will ever find him out.
2. Because he's candid.
3. Chessman.
4. Because he only follows you in sunshine.
5. Ad-vice.
6. Time out of mind.
7. Because the heads were on the wrong end.
8. Spending one's last penny on a purse.
9. Because he is equal to any post.
10. Milestones, you never see two together.
11. A paying one.
12. Sarcasm.
13. Through the customhouse.
14. Give them chairs and let them sit down.
15. It is better not to get into a stew.

Brief Encounter
The Countess is Lady Constance's mother

Four of a Kind
Giggling

Poetical Problem
The first line of the verse gives you LAD, the second ADDER. The complete word is LADDER.

Easy
The letter E.

Which Way?
'Do you live here?'
If you are in Here the answer will be 'Yes,' and if you are in There the answer will be 'No' regardless of the man's residence.

Choral Conundrum
Anthem

Cat-astrophe
The same three cats.

Russian Riddle
Husband and wife.

Jumbled Letters
JUST ONE WORD

Aunts and Uncles
The boy is the man's sister's son.

The Whole Lot
None.

Revolutionary Conundrum
Saratoga (Sara-toga)

False or True
The following statements are false:
1. Untrue
3. Untrue
5. No, he didn't
12. Untrue

15. The duck-billed platypus has.
16. No, it weighs 1¾ lb.
19. Untrue.
24. Wrong, there are 845!

All the others are true.

Key to the Problem

1. A and D   2. D and F
3. C and E   4. C and F
5. A and D   6. B and H

Triangular Terror
Thirty-five triangles.

The Mystery of the Sphinx

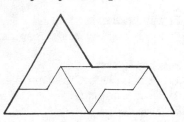

Three Dimensional Shapes
1. A and C   2. B
3. B   4. A
5. D

Before Your Very Eyes
The lines are all the same length.

A Question of Angles
The line A to C is the same length
as the one from B to D; it is the
angles that make them look
longer.

The Distance
The distance is the same.

A Matter of Size
The fields all cover the same area.

Curious Cube
The view of the cube could be from
above or below. The line is perfectly
straight.

Right Angles
Angles A and B are the same.

All Square

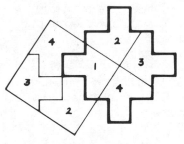

Square and Triangle
Fold the square in half and make
the crease FE. Fold the side AB so
that the point B lies on FE, and you
will get the points G and H from
which you can fold HGJ. While B is

on G, fold back AB on AH, and you will have the line AK. You can now fold the triangle AJK, which is the largest possible equilateral triangle obtainable.

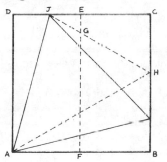

Paper Letter
It is the letter E.

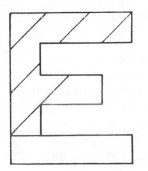

Folding an Octagon
By folding the edge CD over AB we can crease the middle points E and G. In a similar way we can find the points F and H and then crease the square EHGE. Now fold CH on EH and EC on EH, and the point where the creases cross will be the same as 1. Do the same to the other three corners and you will be able to cut out the octagon.

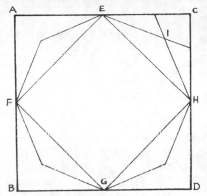

The Biggest Hole in the World
To do this, fold the paper down the centre and make several cuts from each side as shown. Then cut the doubled edge from A to B, leaving parts C and D uncut. The paper will now open up into a large ring.

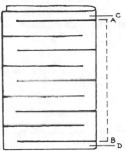

Pinhole Puzzle
The second piece of card appears to have 3 dots too.

Quick Quiz
1. Albumen. If you've put yolk, you've spelt the yellow of an egg!

2. One.

3. A 50p piece and a 10p piece. One of them wasn't a 50p piece, but the other one was!

4. The letter S.

5. Incorrectly.

6. All twelve.

7. 202 each time!

8. 12, of course!

9. January 1st and December 31st fall in the same year every year.

10. Probably!

One Number

1

Unlucky Thirteen

R. All the others are the initial letters of the twelve months of the year.

Lewis Carroll's Puzzles

1. As curly haired James was sleeping in bed,
His brother John gave him a blow on the head.
James opened his eyelids, and spying his brother,
Doubled his fist, and gave him another.
This kind of a box then is not so rare
The lids are the eyelids, the locks are the hair.

2. That salmon and sole Puss should think very grand
Is no such remarkable thing.
For more of these dainties Puss took up her stand;
But when the third sister stretched out her fair hand,
Pray why should Puss swallow her ring?

3. Five seeing and seven blind
Give us twelve, in all, we find;
But all of these, 'tis very plain,
Come into account again.
For take notice, it may be true,
That those blind of one eye are blind of two;
And consider contrariwise,
That to see with your eye you may have your eyes.
So setting one against the other
For a mathematician no great bother
And working the sum you will understand
That sixteen wise men still trouble the land.

4. **1.** You are not a doctor.
2. Dictionaries are valuable.
3. Unselfish people do not save bottle tops.

5. 10 per cent

The Bridge Problem

Connie is the widow.

Death by Drowning

If statement 1 is false: murder but not by Bob.
If statement 2 is false, murder by Bill
If statement 3 is false: accident
This reveals that no two statements can be false. So either none or one is false. From 4, just

one man could not have lied. So no man lied. Since no man lied, it was suicide.

Marriage Lines

1. Mr Foyle's
2. Dark hair
3. Mr Foyle is bald.

Mad Cap

His reasoning was thus: if his cap were white, either one of his rivals would have known that his own was black, for the remaining man's raised hand showed that he saw a black cap, and that couldn't be this knight's if his were white. None of the other rivals dropped their hands to show they knew the colour of their own cap, which means his couldn't be white and therefore must be black.

A Hit or a Miss

If one missile has a chance of missing the target, then all 4 have a chance of missing. Also the target may be hit by 1, 2, 3 or 4 missiles, so Billy was wrong.

MINDBENDERS FOR MASTERMINDS

One Word

NOON

A Time Teaser

9.30

Letters Salad

I C A Z. The other letters read aloud all mean something (I see a sea, I see a bee, I see a jay, I see a ewe), but I C A Z means nothing.

What's Hot?

The sun.

Alarming

Only one hour and a quarter — because your alarm will have woken you at 8.15 that night!

Twin Twister

Jack and Jill are two children from a set of triplets.

Train Trial

The same place from which he jumped.

Charades

Banquet (Bank, wet)

Letter by Letter

All the words can be reduced by one letter at a time and form complete words all the way to a one letter word. For example, brandy, brand, bran, ran, an, a.

That's Cricket

Neither; they both average 3

Plural Puzzle

1. Daughters-in-law
2. Attorneys general
3. Brigadier generals
4. Judge advocates
5. Chargés d'affaires
6. Potatoes

7. Notaries public
8. Laws merchant
9. Opera
10. Pelves
11. Sergeants major
12. Teaspoonfuls
13. Piccolos
14. Tables d'hôte
15. Courts martial
16. Paymasters general
17. Messrs.
18. Mesdames
19. Crises
20. Men of war
21. Lieutenant colonels
22. Banditti
23. Cannon
24. Phenomena
25. Aviatrixes
26. Menservants
27. Oboes
28. Oxen
29. Valets de chambre
30. Data

Special Feature

Each letter of the alphabet appears 3 times.

Underground Stations

1. Westminster
2. Leicester Square
3. Euston
4. Victoria
5. Blackfriars
6. Tower Hill
7. Charing Cross
8. Baker Street
9. Kingsway
10. Green Park
11. Strand
12. Elephant & Castle

Beauty Queens

Caroline the blonde hairdresser is the oldest. Amelia the brunette receptionist comes next. Bernice the redheaded typist is next.

Find the Number

4368

All in the Family

1. 27 pairs of cousins.
2. 12 pairs of father and son.
3. 12 pairs of brothers.
4. 18 pairs of uncle and nephew.
5. 9 pairs of grandfather and grandson.
6. 13 people altogether.

Liquid Refreshment

First you fill the 3 pint container. Empty it into the 5 pint container. Fill the 3 pint container again. Empty it into the 5 pint container until the latter is full. Now one pint will remain in the 3 pint container.

Triangular Trouble

1.

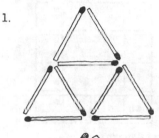

2.

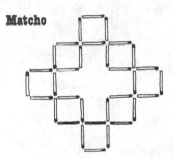

3.

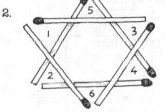

4.

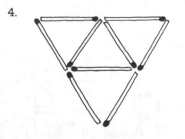

5.

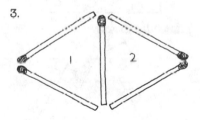

Matcho

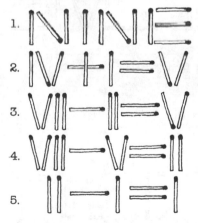

MatheMATCHics

1. NINE

2. IV + II = V

3. VII — II = V

4. VII — V = II

5. II — I = I

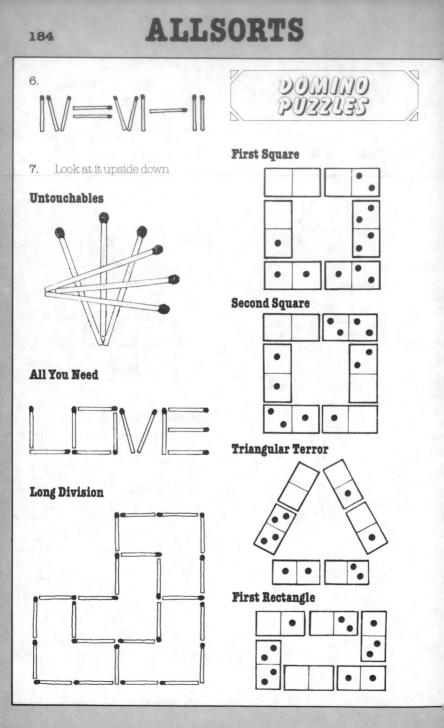

6.

7. Look at it upside down

Untouchables

All You Need

Long Division

DOMINO PUZZLES

First Square

Second Square

Triangular Terror

First Rectangle

The Three Rectangles

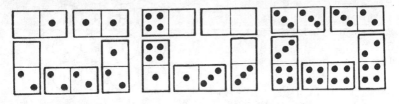

Giant Square

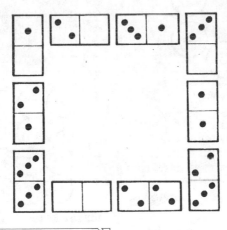

COIN PUZZLES

Cross Challenge

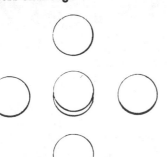

There are two coins in the middle.

Square Challenge

There are two coins at each corner.

Circular Challenge

Here are your three moves:
1. Move 4 to touch 5 and 6
2. Move 5 to touch 1 and 2
3. Move 1 to touch 5 and 4

The circle should now look like this:

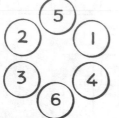

Pyramid Challenge

Here are your three moves:
1. Move 1 to below the bottom row and place it between and under 8 and 9.
2. Move 7 up two rows and place it to the left of 2.
3. Move 10 up two rows and place it to the right of 3.

The H Problem

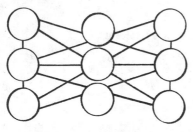

Sixteen Coins

Put your first and second fingers on the two asterisked coins and bring them round into the positions indicated by the dotted lines:

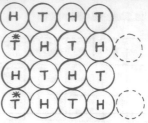

Now, with your fingers still on the same two coins, push the six coins (that's to say the three coins in the second row and the three coins in the bottom row) to the left and you will end up with the columns looking just as you want them:

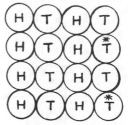

Six in a Row

Here are your three moves:
1. Move coins 1 and 2 to the right of 6
2. Move coins 6 and 1 to the right of 2
3. Move coins 3 and 4 to the right of 5

Eight in a Row

Here are your four moves:
1. Move coins 6 and 7 to the left of 1
2. Move coins 3 and 4 to the right of 5
3. Move coins 7 and 1 to the right of 2
4. Move coins 4 and 8 to the right of 6

Head Over Heels

Count always in the same direction, missing out one coin each time before starting the next count.

Nine-a-side

Here are twenty-eight coins in a square, with nine coins on each side. At each of the four corners to the square there are two coins and in the centre of each of the four sides there are five coins.

Here are twenty-four coins in a square, with nine coins on each side. The square is made up of eight piles of coins, with three coins in each pile.

Here are twenty coins in a square, with nine coins on each side. At each of the four corners of the square there are four coins and in the centre of each of the four sides there is one coin.

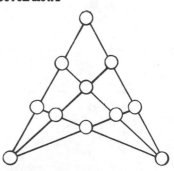

Odd Lines

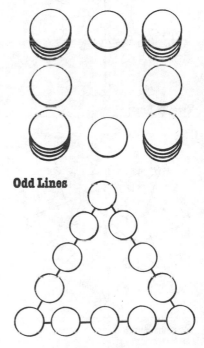

Seven Rows

Nine Rows

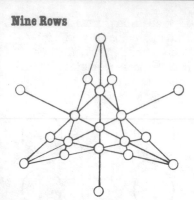

Twelve Rows

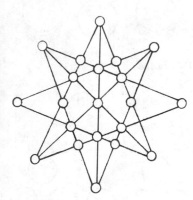

Fifteen Rows

TANGRAMS

Shapely Tangrams

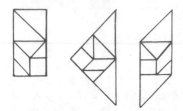

Number Tangrams

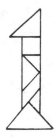

Alphabetical Tangrams

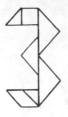

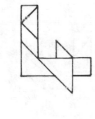

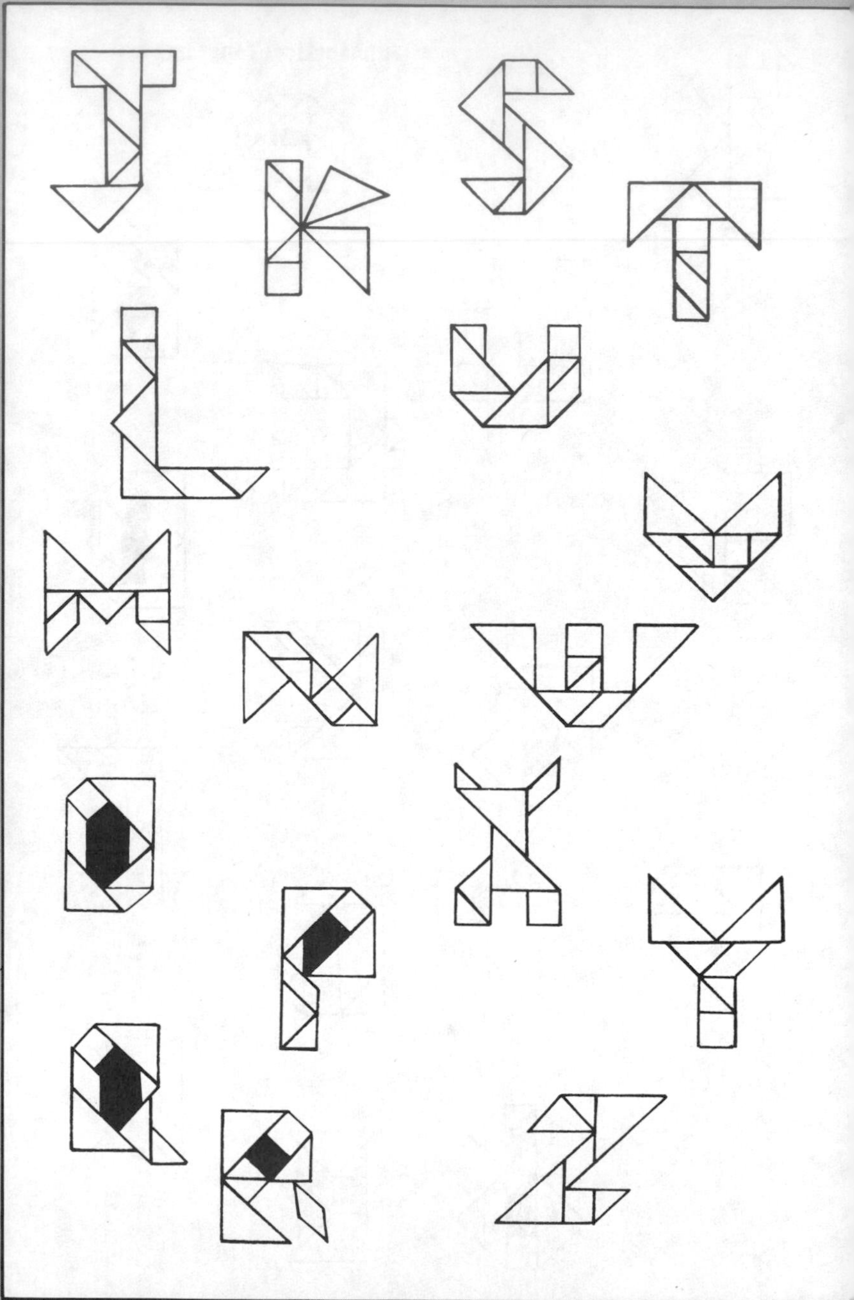

MIXED BAG

The Missing Letters
Q

What's What?
1. A bald head.
2. Tomorrow
3. Your breath
4. A pack of cards
5. The letter E
6. A sponge
7. Silence
8. Your future
9. A stitch
10. A hole
11. A pen
12. A coffin
13. Their own nose
14. A right angle
15. A candle
16. A kiss
17. A carpet
18. Down – like swan's down
19. The motorway
20. Holes

My Three Sons
Yvan. The Lawyer's name is 'bar' spelt backwards, the soldier's name is 'army' spelt backwards, so the sailor's name is 'navy' spelt backwards.

Oddition

```
  11
   1
   1
+  1
────
  14
```

Musical Meanings
1. **Presto** means fast.
2. **Adagio** means very slowly.
3. **Largo** means in a slow, dignified style.
4. **Fortissimo** means very loud.
5. **Dolce** means sweetly.
6. **Crescendo** means increasing the volume slowly.

Weak Word
Strengthlessness

Unpunctuated
1. He said that that 'that' that that woman said, ought to have been 'which'.

2. It was 'and' I said, not 'but'.

3. The murderer spoke angrily. Half an hour after he was hanged.

4. Time flies? You cannot. They pass by at such irregular intervals.

5. Esau Wood saw a saw saw wood as no other wood-saw Wood saw would saw wood. Of all the wood-saws Wood ever saw saw wood, Wood never saw a wood-saw that would saw wood as the wood-saw Wood saw saw wood would saw wood, and I never saw a wood-saw that would saw wood as the wood-saw Wood saw would saw, until I saw Wood saw wood with the wood-saw Esau Wood saw saw wood.

Composers' Corner
These are the five phoneys:
Rudolph Von Smettow
Hector Adolph Buzzi

Giuseppe Pizzo
Igor Plinplonski
Kurt Barsolova

The Nelson Touch
East. He begins facing West. Once he has made a right turn he is facing North. He then makes an about turn and is facing South. Finally he turns left and is facing East.

What and Where?
1. The Leaning Tower of Pisa – Italy
2. The Taj Mahal – India
3. Buckingham Palace – England
4. The Niagara Falls – USA/Canada
5. The Eiffel Tower – France
6. The Great Wall – China
7. The Rio Grande – USA
8. The Golden Gate Bridge – USA
9. Cleopatra's Needle – England
10. The Empire State Building – USA

Top Ten
1. Six of one, half a dozen of the other.
2. Spinach (sp in ach)
3. Mary Overton
4. You understand you are under oath
5. *Much Ado About Nothing*
6. A bad spell of weather
7. Continue (c on t in u)
8. I understand you undertake to overthrow my undertaking.
9. All in one
10. Oh, I see you are empty.

Finally

THE END

Dotty Problems

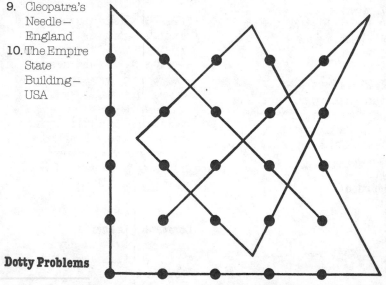